ADDISON-WESLEY

QUEST 2000

EXPLORING MATHEMATICS

EXTRA PRACTICE AND TESTING MASTERS

Addison-Wesley Publishers Limited

Don Mills, Ontario • Reading, Massachusetts

Menlo Park, California • New York

Wokingham, England • Amsterdam

Bonn • Sydney • Singapore • Madrid

San Juan • Paris • Seoul • Milan

Mexico City • Taipei

GRADE 4

Printed and bound in Canada.

ISBN 0-201-68277-X

This book is printed on acid-free paper.

C D E F – PC – 02 01 00 99 98

CONTENTS

1-1	Collecting Data	1
1-1	Graphing Data	2
1-2	Analyzing Line Plots	3
1-3	Creating Line Plots	4
1-3	Analyzing Data	5
1-4	Exploring Average	6
1-4	Representing Data	7
Unit 1 Test 1		8
Unit 1 Test 2		9
Unit 1 Test 3		10
2-1	Estimating and Counting	11
2-1	Using Number Sense	12
2-2	Writing Numbers (1)	13
2-2	Understanding Numbers	14
2-3	Writing Numbers (2)	15
2-3	Reading and Writing Numbers	16
2-4	Representing Numbers (1)	17
2-4	Representing Numbers (2)	18
2-5	Naming Numbers	19
2-5	Using Place Value (1)	20
2-6	Using Place Value (2)	21
2-6	Comparing and Ordering Numbers	22
Unit 2 Test 1		23
Unit 2 Test 2		24
Unit 2 Test 3		25
Unit 2 Test 4		26
3-1	Exploring Triangles	27
3-2	Sorting Triangles	28
3-3	Identifying Triangles	29
3-4	Creating Quadrilaterals	30
3-5	Finding Figures within Figures	31
Unit 3 Test 1		32
Unit 3 Test 2		33
Unit 3 Test 3		34
4-1	Adding	35
4-1	Subtracting	36
4-2	Adding and Subtracting (1)	37
4-2	Adding and Subtracting (2)	38
4-2	Estimating to Solve Problems	39
4-2	Using Addition and Subtraction to Solve Problems	40
4-3	Estimating Sums and Differences (1)	41
4-3	Estimating Sums and Differences (2)	42
4-4	Exploring Multiplication (1)	43
4-4	Exploring Multiplication (2)	44
4-5	Connecting Multiplication and Division (1)	45
4-5	Connecting Multiplication and Division (2)	46
4-6	Skip Counting	47
4-6	Exploring Division	48
4-6	Multiplying and Dividing (1)	49
4-7	Multiplying and Dividing (2)	50
4-7	Multiplying and Dividing (3)	51
4-7	Multiplying and Dividing (4)	52
4-8	Solving Problems (1)	53
4-8	Solving Problems (2)	54
Unit 4 Test 1		55
Unit 4 Test 2		56
Unit 4 Test 3		57
Unit 4 Test 4		58
5-1	Finding Perimeter (1)	59
5-1	Finding Perimeter (2)	60
5-2	Same Area, Different Perimeters	61
5-3	Finding Area (1)	62
5-3	Finding Area (2)	63
5-4	Finding the Areas of Right Triangles	64
5-5	Finding Area in Square Centimetres (1)	65
5-5	Finding Area in Square Centimetres (2)	66
5-6	Estimating and Measuring Area	67
Unit 5 Test 1		68
Unit 5 Test 2		69
Unit 5 Test 3		70

CONTENTS *continued*

6-1	Exploring Halves	71
6-1	Naming Fractions	72
6-2	Finding Equivalent Fractions (1)	73
6-2	Finding Equivalent Fractions (2)	74
6-3	Comparing Fractions (1)	75
6-3	Comparing Fractions (2)	76
6-4	Naming Fractions of Sets (1)	77
6-5	Naming Fractions of Sets (2)	78
6-6	Naming Fraction Tenths and Hundredths	79
6-6	Showing Tenths and Hundredths	80
6-7	Naming Fractions and Decimals (1)	81
6-7	Naming Fractions and Decimals (2)	82
6-8	Naming Fractions and Decimals (3)	83
6-8	Connecting Fractions and Decimals	84
	Unit 6 Test 1	85
	Unit 6 Test 2	86
	Unit 6 Test 3	87
	Unit 6 Test 4	88
7-1	Using Data	89
7-1	Multiplying by Multiples of Ten	90
7-2	Multiplying Using Arrays (1)	91
7-2	Multiplying Using Arrays (2)	92
7-3	Using Partial Products	93
7-3	Multiplying Whole Numbers	94
7-4	Using Patterns to Multiply	95
7-4	Problem Solving (1)	96
7-5	Estimating Products (1)	97
7-5	Estimating Products (2)	98
7-6	Multiplying (1)	99
7-6	Multiplying (2)	100
7-7	Dividing Using Arrays	101
7-7	Dividing Whole Numbers	102
7-8	Problem Solving (2)	103
7-8	Problem Solving (3)	104
7-9	Dividing (1)	105
7-9	Dividing (2)	106
	Unit 7 Test 1	107
	Unit 7 Test 2	108
	Unit 7 Test 3	109
	Unit 7 Test 4	110
8-1	Identifying Lines	111
8-1	Identifying Symmetry	112
8-2	Comparing Geometric Solids	113
8-2	Relating Nets to Solids	114
8-3	Identifying Quadrilaterals	115
8-3	Locating Figures on a Grid	116
8-4	Using Maps	117
	Unit 8 Test 1	118
	Unit 8 Test 2	119
	Unit 8 Test 3	120
9-1	Identifying Patterns	121
9-1	Using Patterns	122
9-2	Using T-Tables (1)	123
9-2	Using T-Tables (2)	124
	Unit 9 Test 1	125
	Unit 9 Test 2	126
10-1	Exploring Outcomes	127
10-2	Predicting Outcomes	128
10-3	Finding All Outcomes	129
10-4	Finding Combinations	130
10-5	Analyzing Outcomes	131
	Unit 10 Test 1	132
	Unit 10 Test 2	133
	Unit 10 Test 3	134
11-1	Measuring in Centimetres (1)	135
11-1	Measuring in Centimetres (2)	136
11-2	Measuring in Millimetres (1)	137
11-2	Measuring in Millimetres (2)	138
11-3	Measuring in Metres (1)	139
11-3	Measuring in Metres (2)	140
11-4	Measuring Capacity (1)	141
11-4	Measuring Capacity (2)	142
11-5	Measuring Mass (1)	143
11-5	Measuring Mass (2)	144
	Unit 11 Test 1	145
	Unit 11 Test 2	146
	Unit 11 Test 3	147
	Unit 11 Test 4	148
	Skills Bank	149–182
	Index of Skills	183–184

Collecting Data

You want to open a store to sell interesting and unusual socks. You want to collect data about socks to make your store popular with customers.

Write five questions you might ask to collect data about socks.

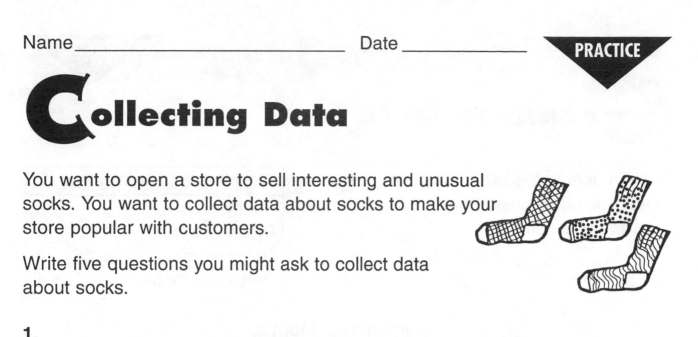

1. _____

2. _____

3. _____

4. _____

5. _____

6. Explain how you would collect and organize the data. Include the number of people you would ask and how you would select them.

_____

_____

7. Interview five people using your questions. Organize the data. Make three statements about your findings.

_____

_____

_____

Grade 4
Use with Unit 1, Activity 1.

1

Name_____   Date _____

raphing Data

Use the data in the table. Complete the pictograph. Then use the graph to answer the questions.

This Month's Weather	
Sunny days	12
Cloudy days	6
Rainy days	8
Partly cloudy days	4

Weather This Month

Sunny	☀	
Cloudy	☁	
Rainy	🌧	
Partly cloudy	⛅	

1 symbol = 2 days

1. Were most days this month sunny? Explain. _____

_____

2. How many more days were rainy than partly cloudy?_____

Which gives you the answer more quickly, the pictograph or the table? Explain.

_____

3. Suppose next month's weather is similar to this month's. Estimate the number of days you might expect rainy weather. about _____ days

2

Grade 4
Use with Unit 1, Activity 1.

Analyzing Line Plots

People in Marisol's apartment building get lots of unaddressed mail. Unaddressed mail includes flyers, catalogues, and other advertisements. Marisol gathered data about how much unaddressed mail each family in her building received yesterday. This line plot shows the data.

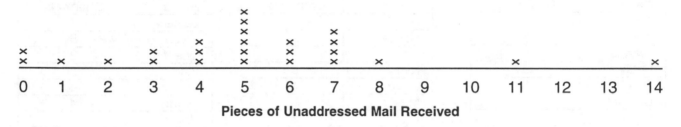

Pieces of Unaddressed Mail Received

Use the line plot to answer the questions.

1. How many families received four pieces of unaddressed mail? _____

2. What number came up most often (mode)?_____

3. Why did Marisol include a 0 on her line plot?

_____

4. How would you describe the spread (range) of the data?

_____

5. How many families did Marisol survey? How do you know?

_____

6. What conclusions could Marisol make about the amount of unaddressed mail her neighbours received?

_____

_____

Name_____ Date _____

Creating Line Plots

Most people don't watch all the TV channels available. Seth asked his classmates how many channels they watch regularly. He collected these data.

Number of Channels Watched Regularly

Name	Number of Channels
Andy	2
Aurora	5
Brenda	5
Betsy	3
Chazz	3
Danitra	1
Evan	4
Fawn	3

Name	Number of Channels
Graziella	0
Hassan	8
Irina	3
Kim	6
Lloyd	4
Malka	5
Ng	2
Noreen	2

Name	Number of Channels
Olivia	4
Pryce	5
Quentin	2
Rico	2
Seth	4
Timmy	4
Ursula	4
Victoria	5

1. Organize the data in a line plot.

2. What is the median? _____   **3.** What is the mode? _____

4. What do you notice about the median and the mode for these data?

_____

5. What can you say about the TV-watching habits of students in Seth's class?

_____

_____

6. What does the table show that the line plot does not?

_____

_____

7. What does the line plot show that the table does not?

_____

© Addison-Wesley Publishers Limited

Grade 4
Use with Unit 1, Activity 3.

PRACTICE

Analyzing Data

Leung spent two hours building card houses. Each time a house collapsed, he counted the number of cards he was able to balance before they fell. He made a line plot to show his results.

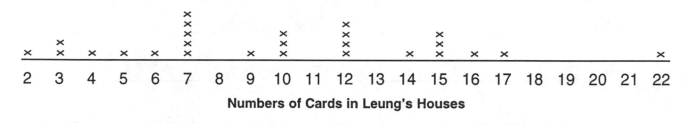

Numbers of Cards in Leung's Houses

Use the line plot to answer the questions.

1. How many card houses did Leung build? How do you know?

_____

2. How many cards did his most successful
house contain before it fell?   _____

3. What was the least number of cards he
was able to balance?   _____

4. How many cards was Leung able to balance
most often (mode)?   _____

5. What was the middle (median) number of
cards he was able to balance?   _____

6. Suppose Leung keeps practising. A month from now he collects the same
data. How might the new line plot look? Explain.

_____

_____

Exploring Average

Analyze each set of data.

1. Data: | 38, 44, 84, 33, 56 |

The median is _____.

The mean is_____.

2. Data: | 328, 449, 123, 328 |

The mean is _____.

The mode is _____.

3. Data: | 68, 37, 50, 45, 25 |

The median is _____.

The mean is_____.

4. Data: | 233, 219, 111, 107, 200 |

The mean is _____.

The median is_____.

5. Data: | 1, 4, 5, 2, 2, 5, 1, 5 |

Which is greater, the median or the mode? _____

6. Data: | 30, 15, 47, 28 |

Which is greater, the mean or the median? _____

7. Data: | 16, 23, 16, 34, 16 |

Which is greater, the mode or the mean? _____

Grade 4
Use with Unit 1, Activity 4.

Representing Data

Every feature film begins with previews of coming attractions. The table shows the length of a film and the number of previews shown before the film begins at a cinema.

Film Title	Length (in minutes)	Number of Previews
Rain Forest Follies	103	4
The Secret Turtle	95	5
The Brave Little Yogurt	100	4
Bunnies on the Run	87	5
Look Who's Chirping, Too	110	3
Revenge of the Gerbils	98	4
Square Dances with Wolves	135	2

Use the data in the table to answer the questions.

1. What is the shortest movie length?_____

2. What is the longest movie length? _____

3. What is the mean length of the movies?_____

   Which film length is closest to the mean length?_____

   _____

4. Which film's length equals the median length of the movies?

   _____

5. Make a line plot of the data about the number of previews.

6. What is the mode of the previews? _____

7. What relationship do you see between the length of a film and the number of previews shown with it?

_____

Unit 1 (Collecting and Analyzing Data)

Test 1

Suppose your class wants to raise money for a trip.
You decide to sell snacks at school.

1. What other information would help you plan your fundraising project?

_____

_____

2. What questions would you ask to get the information?

_____

_____

_____

3. Whom would you ask?

_____

_____

4. How would you collect and organize the data?

_____

_____

_____

5. How would you display the data? Explain your choices.

_____

_____

© Addison-Wesley Publishers Limited

Name_____ Date _____

Unit 1 (Collecting and Analyzing Data)

Test 2

Use the graph.

1. How were the data collected?

_____

_____

2. How many times was number 3 rolled?

_____

3. Which numbers came up the most often and the least often?

_____

4. Which two numbers came up the same number of times?

_____

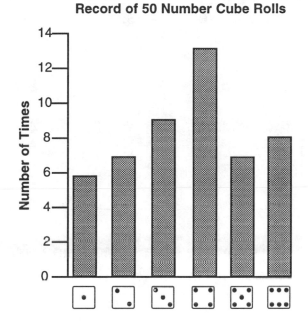

Record of 50 Number Cube Rolls

5. Kate put a penny, a nickel, and a dime in a bag and shook it. She pulled out a coin, recorded the result, then put the coin back in the bag. She did this 50 times. Here is her data. Use it to make a graph.

Number of Outcomes	17	19	14

Grade 4
Use after Unit 1.

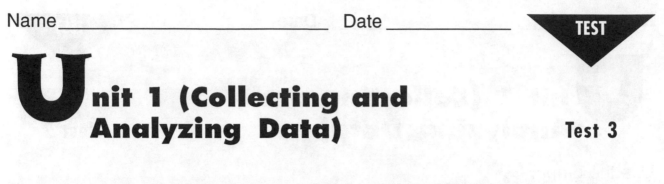

Unit 1 (Collecting and Analyzing Data)

Test 3

Jana asked her classmates how many books they read over the summer. Here are their replies.

3	6	1	10	8	4	12	0
2	4	7	3	4	9	2	5
4	7	5	3	5	10	4	9

1. Display the data using a line plot.

2. Write three statements about the data.

_____

_____

_____

_____

© Addison-Wesley Publishers Limited

Grade 4
Use after Unit 1.

Estimating and Counting

1. About how many pennies would cover this page? Circle an estimate.

   about 80   about 180   about 380

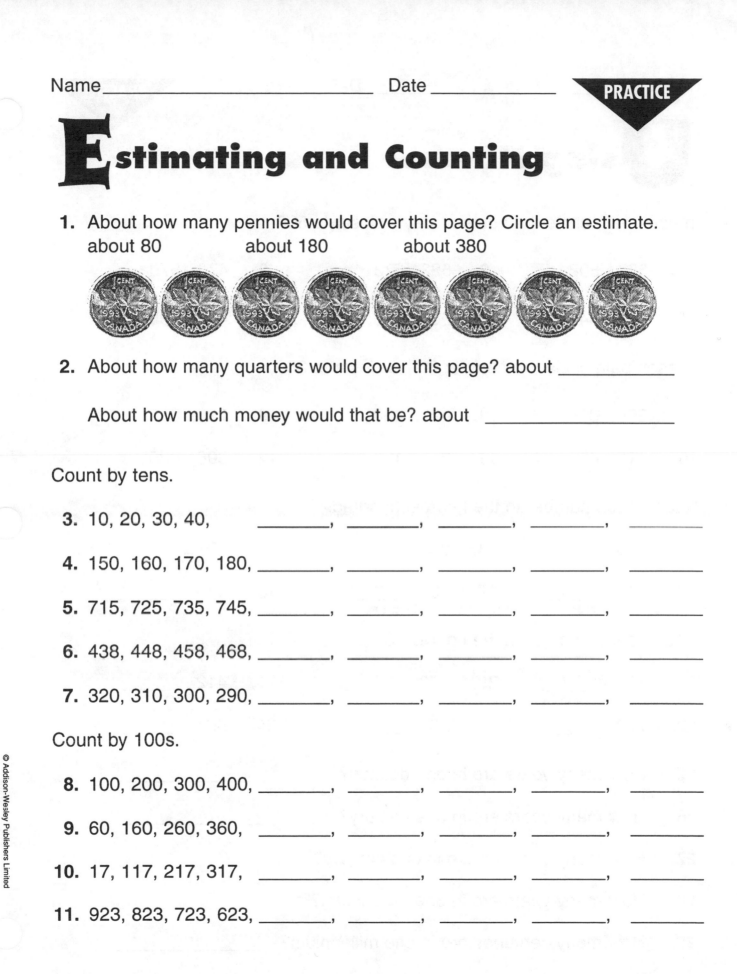

2. About how many quarters would cover this page? about _____

   About how much money would that be? about _____

Count by tens.

3. 10, 20, 30, 40, _____, _____, _____, _____, _____

4. 150, 160, 170, 180, _____, _____, _____, _____, _____

5. 715, 725, 735, 745, _____, _____, _____, _____, _____

6. 438, 448, 458, 468, _____, _____, _____, _____, _____

7. 320, 310, 300, 290, _____, _____, _____, _____, _____

Count by 100s.

8. 100, 200, 300, 400, _____, _____, _____, _____, _____

9. 60, 160, 260, 360, _____, _____, _____, _____, _____

10. 17, 117, 217, 317, _____, _____, _____, _____, _____

11. 923, 823, 723, 623, _____, _____, _____, _____, _____

Name_____ Date _____  PRACTICE

Using Number Sense

In each pair, circle the number that is closer to 500.

1. 580, 508   **2.** 523, 573   **3.** 470, 570

4. 324, 342   **5.** 909, 910   **6.** 445, 495

In each pair, circle the number that is closer to 360.

7. 365, 356   **8.** 427, 430   **9.** 726, 835

10. 215, 415   **11.** 215, 125   **12.** 306, 630

Round each number to the nearest hundred.

13. 215 _____   **14.** 251 _____   **15.** 397 _____

16. 717 _____   **17.** 160 _____   **18.** 945 _____

Round each number to the nearest ten.

19. 78 _____   **20.** 176 _____   **21.** 412 _____

22. 789 _____   **23.** 266 _____   **24.** 501 _____

25. How many years are in one decade?   _____

26. How many years are in one century?   _____

27. How many decades are in one century?   _____

28. How many years are in one millennium?   _____

29. How many centuries are in one millennium?   _____

Grade 4
Use with Unit 2, Activity 1.

Writing Numbers (1)

Write the numeral for each group of blocks. Then write the number in words.

1.

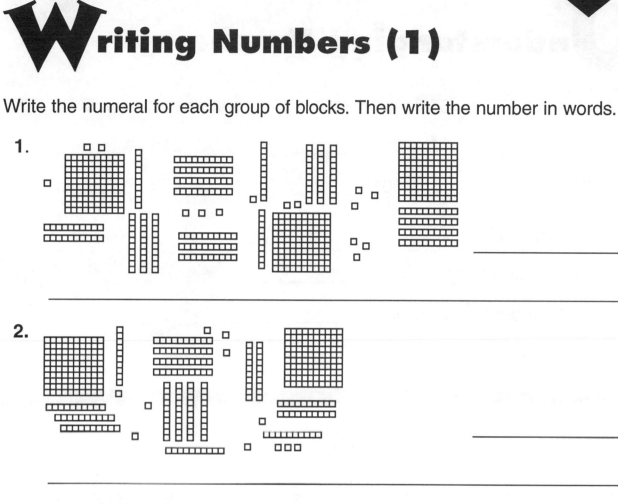

_____

_____

2.

_____

_____

3.

_____

_____

4.

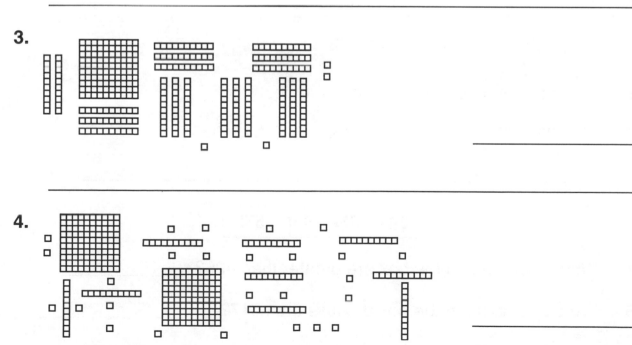

_____

_____

Understanding Numbers

What is the value of the 5 in each number? Write your answer as 5, 50, or 500.

1. 580 _____ **2.** 985 _____ **3.** 215 _____

4. 152 _____ **5.** 501 _____ **6.** 650 _____

Write the numeral for each.

7. three hundred fifty _____

8. eight hundred sixty-seven _____

9. two hundred three _____

10. one hundred seventeen _____

Circle the greater number in each pair.

11. 47, 77 **12.** 860, 608

13. 565, 569 **14.** 342, 432

List each set of numbers from least to greatest.

15. 879, 856, 876 **16.** 315, 345, 333

_____ _____

| 341 677 465 572 |

17. Which numbers in the box are greater than 426? _____

18. Which numbers in the box are less than 517? _____

Grade 4
Use with Unit 2, Activity 2.

PRACTICE

Writing Numbers (2)

Write the number shown by each group of blocks.

1.
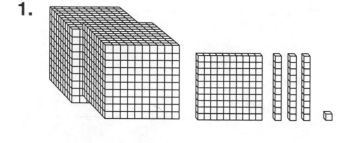

_____

2.
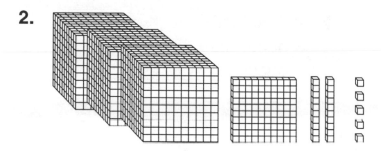

_____

Write the numeral for each.

3. 7 thousands, 2 hundreds, 6 tens, 3 ones _____

4. 3 thousands, 7 hundreds, 5 tens, 1 one _____

5. eight thousand four hundred sixty-seven _____

6. six thousand thirty-five _____

7. nine thousand three hundred two _____

8. two thousand seventy _____

9. eight thousand two hundred nine _____

10. 3 thousands, 4 hundreds, 2 tens, 9 ones _____

11. 7 thousands, 5 tens, 3 ones _____

Grade 4
Use with Unit 2, Activity 3.

Name_____ Date _____

Reading and Writing Numbers

Write the numeral for each.

1. 5 thousands
   3 hundreds
   6 tens
   2 ones _____

2. 7 hundreds
   5 tens
   8 ones _____

3. 6 thousands
   3 tens
   9 ones _____

4. 2 thousands
   8 hundreds
   4 ones _____

5. four hundred eighty-seven _____

6. six thousand two hundred twenty-two _____

7. five thousand nine hundred forty _____

8. nine thousand fifty-nine _____

9. seven thousand six hundred five _____

Write each number in words.

10. 320 _____

11. 4816 _____

12. 1095 _____

13. 9510 _____

14. 8760 _____

Grade 4
Use with Unit 2, Activity 3.

Name_____ Date _____

Representing Numbers (1)

Use the charts. Show 4 different ways to make each number.
Each chart has one example to get you started.

1. 456

hundreds	tens	ones
4	4	16

2. 3173

thousands	hundreds	tens	ones
2	11	7	3

3. Make your own chart that shows hundreds, tens, and ones.
Record in your chart four possible combinations for 482.

Name_____ Date _____

Representing Numbers (2)

Write the numeral for each group of blocks. Then write the number in words.

1.

_____ _____

2.

_____ _____

| 50 | 100 | 250 | 500 | 1000 | 2000 |

Combine the numbers in the box to make each number given below.
Use the numbers in the box as many times as you like.
Build each number three different ways.

3. 1800 = 500 + 500 + 500 + 250 + 50

1800 = _____

1800 = _____

1800 = _____

4. 4250 = _____

4250 = _____

4250 = _____

Grade 4
Use with Unit 2, Activity 4.

Name_____ Date _____

Naming Numbers

Write the letter for each number word next to the matching numeral.

1. 15 340 _____ **A** fifty-three thousand two hundred

2. 50 534 _____ **B** five thousand four hundred

3. 53 200 _____ **C** five thousand five hundred thirty-four

4. 32 050 _____ **D** fifty thousand five hundred thirty-four

5. 5534 _____ **E** fifteen thousand three hundred forty

6. 5400 _____ **F** thirty-two thousand fifty

Write the numeral for each.

7. five thousand six hundred twelve _____

8. thirty thousand eight hundred forty _____

9. seventeen thousand nine hundred thirty-five _____

10. twenty thousand five hundred _____

11. eight hundred eighty _____

12. nineteen thousand forty-three _____

13. 3000 + 100 + 30 + 6 _____

14. 80 000 + 800 + 10 + 5 _____

15. 50 000 + 4000 + 80 _____

16. 10 000 + 5000 + 600 _____

Grade 4
Use with Unit 2, Activity 5.

Name_____ Date _____

Using Place Value (1)

Write the digit for the given place in the numeral 70 258.

1. thousands _____

2. tens _____

3. ten thousands _____

4. hundreds _____

5. ones _____

What is the value of the 6 in each numeral?
Write your answer as 6, 60, 600, 6000, or 60 000.

6. 51 673 _____

7. 62 048 _____

8. 8756 _____

9. 7653 _____

10. 35 269 _____

11. 16 300 _____

Circle the greater number in each pair.

12. 323 or 423

13. 1560 or 1506

14. 1976 or 1076

15. 4586 or 3991

16. 46 896 or 46 921

17. 59 003 or 58 300

18. Use all the digits in the box.
Make a number with 7 thousands._____

7		1
	6	
5		3

19. Use all the digits in the box. Make a
number with 7 hundreds and 15 thousands. _____

20

Grade 4
Use with Unit 2, Activity 5.

Using Place Value (2)

Use the digits 0 to 9. Write numbers with five digits.
Use each digit only once in a numeral.

1. Greatest number

   _____

2. Greatest even number

   _____

3. Greatest number with 8
   in the hundreds place

   _____

4. Greatest even number with 2
   in the thousands place

   _____

5. Least number

   _____

6. Least number with 4
   in the ten thousands place

   _____

7. Least odd number with 9
   in the thousands place

   _____

8. Least even number greater
   than 50 000

   _____

Sort your numbers in this chart.

	Greater than 45 000	45 000 or less
Even		
Odd		

Name_____ Date _____

Comparing and Ordering Numbers

The table shows the populations of eight cities.
Circle the city in each pair with the
greater population.

City	Population
Nowberg	99 442
Little Town	3 900
Low River	95 963
Tower City	82 061
Cartville	49 542
Motorton	10 228
Treetop	45 553
Rainfield	84 885

1. Nowberg or Low River

2. Nowberg or Cartville

3. Cartville or Motorton

Circle the least population in each set.

4. 99 442   or   84 885   or   82 061

5. 45 553   or   84 885   or   49 542

6. List the populations in order
   from greatest to least.

   _____

   _____

   _____

7. Round each population to the nearest thousand.

   99 442 _____   3900 _____

   95 963 _____   82 061 _____

   49 542 _____   10 228 _____

   45 553 _____   84 885 _____

Unit 2
(Representing Numbers)

Test 1

Write the number shown by each group of blocks.

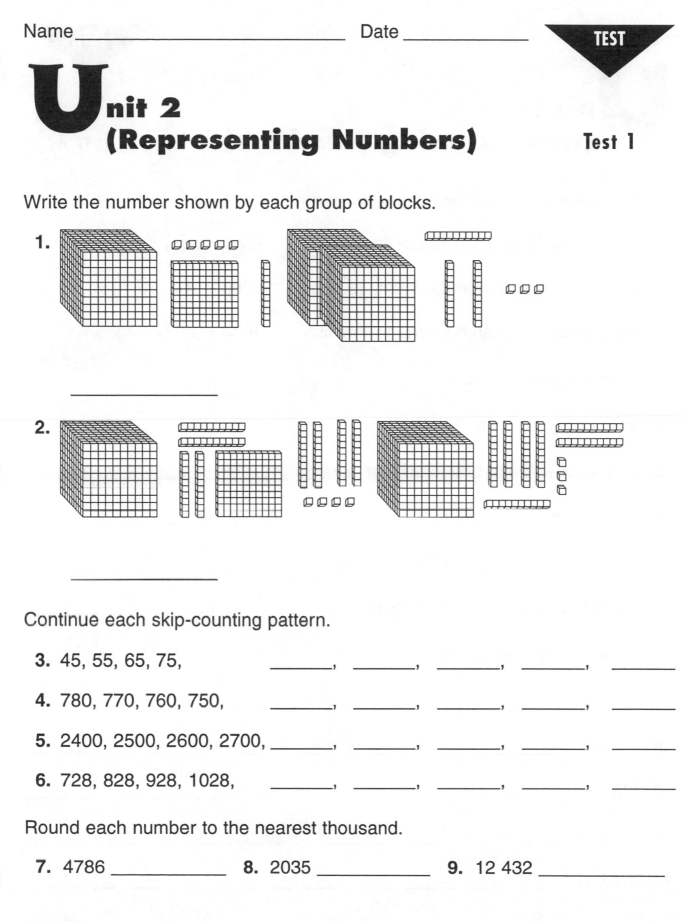

1.

_____

2.

_____

Continue each skip-counting pattern.

3. 45, 55, 65, 75, _____, _____, _____, _____, _____

4. 780, 770, 760, 750, _____, _____, _____, _____, _____

5. 2400, 2500, 2600, 2700, _____, _____, _____, _____, _____

6. 728, 828, 928, 1028, _____, _____, _____, _____, _____

Round each number to the nearest thousand.

7. 4786 _____   **8.** 2035 _____   **9.** 12 432 _____

TEST

Unit 2
(Representing Numbers)   Test 2

1. Circle the numbers that represent 5725.

   five thousand seven hundred fifteen   500 + 700 + 25

   5 thousands, 7 hundreds, 1 ten, 15 ones   5000 + 700 + 20 + 5

   five thousand seven hundred twenty-five   4000 + 1700 + 25

Write the numeral for each.

2. seven hundred sixty-five   _____

3. one thousand eight hundred four   _____

4. eight thousand seventy-six   _____

5. twelve thousand one hundred thirteen   _____

6. fifty thousand two hundred twenty-five   _____

Write each number in words.

7.   785   _____

8.   2484   _____

9.   3098   _____

10. 98 483   _____

11. 70 210   _____

Grade 4
Use after Unit 2.

Unit 2 (Representing Numbers)

What is the value of the 9 in each number?
Write your answer as 9, 90, 900, 9000, or 90 000.

1. 9356 _____

2. 89 023_____

3. 72 394 _____

4. 12 609_____

5. 90 218 _____

6. 98 760_____

Complete.

7. 2000 + 30 + 4 = _____

8. 70 000 + 4000 + 200 + 9 = _____

9. _____ + 2000 + 500 + 30 = 82 530

10. 30 000 + _____ + _____ + 3 = 30 743

11. Use all the digits in the box.
Make a number with 5 ten thousands. _____

0		4
	8	
5		3

12. Use all the digits in the box.
Make a number with 5 hundreds and 0 thousands. _____

Write the numeral for each.

13. 1 ten thousand, 6 thousands, 3 hundreds _____

14. 9 ten thousands, 15 tens, 3 ones _____

15. 2 thousands, 8 hundreds, 25 ones _____

16. 45 thousands, 7 hundreds, 4 tens _____

Unit 2
(Representing Numbers)   Test 4

Circle the greater number in each pair.

1. 726 or 834

2. 6509 or 6590

3. 1493 or 4193

4. 19 095 or 18 996

5. 82 040 or 83 730

6. 59 160 or 69 130

Write > (greater than) or < (less than) in each box to make the statement true.

7. 336 ☐ 337

8. 6000 ☐ 5900

9. 3816 ☐ 3755

10. 40 993 ☐ 40 879

11. 21 676 ☐ 51 676

12. 78 451 ☐ 78 471

List the numbers in each set in order from least to greatest.

13. 468, 761, 532

14. 4682, 2801, 8329

_____

_____

15. 18 960, 18 096, 18 906

16. 51 580, 53 505, 95 214

_____

_____

Use the digits 7, 4, 3, 2, 9, and 5.
Use each digit only once in each number.

17. Make the greatest number with four digits. _____

18. Make the least number with four digits. _____

19. Make the greatest number with five digits. _____

20. Make the least number with five digits. _____

26

Grade 4
Use after Unit 2.

Exploring Triangles

The table lists side lengths for triangles.
Decide whether each set of side lengths could form a triangle.
Use any method you wish to check your solutions.

	Side	Side	Side
1.	10 cm	13 cm	12 cm
2.	5 cm	8 cm	5 cm
3.	2 cm	6 cm	3 cm
4.	20 cm	10 cm	12 cm
5.	9 cm	9 cm	9 cm
6.	5 cm	15 cm	9 cm
7.	13 cm	12 cm	5 cm

Can a triangle be made?

_____

_____

_____

_____

_____

_____

_____

Complete the table so that each set of three sides will form a triangle.

	Side	Side	Side
8.	6 cm	7 cm	___ cm
9.	10 cm	___ cm	3 cm
10.	___ cm	9 cm	12 cm
11.	4 cm	___ cm	___ cm
12.	35 cm	41 cm	___ cm

Name_____ Date _____

Sorting Triangles

Sort the triangles.
Colour triangles like A red.
Colour triangles like B blue.
Colour triangles like C green.

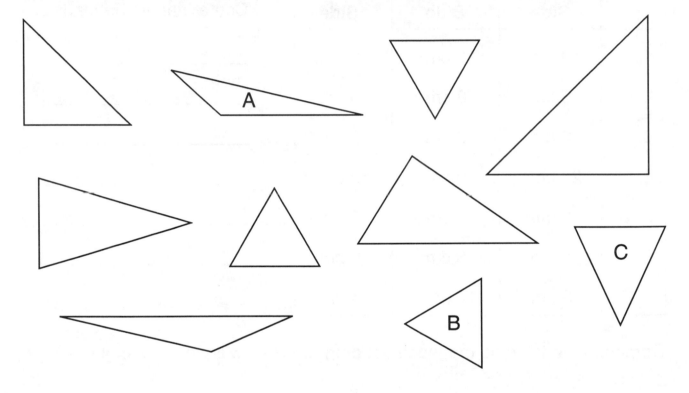

Draw an isosceles triangle here.	Draw an equilateral triangle here.	Draw a scalene triangle here.
Is it like triangle A, B, or C?	Is it like triangle A, B, or C?	Is it like triangle A, B, or C?

Grade 4
Use with Unit 3, Activity 2.

Identifying Triangles

Write the letter of the triangle described by each sentence.
Then tell what kind of triangle it is.

1. It has three angles less than a right angle.
It has two sides the same length.

A

_____   _____

2. It has one right angle.
All sides are different lengths.

B

_____   _____

3. It has one angle greater than a right angle.
It has two sides the same length.

C

_____   _____

4. It has one right angle and
two sides the same length.

D

_____   _____

5. It has three sides the same length.

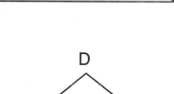

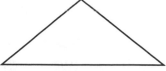
E

_____   _____

Creating Quadrilaterals

Draw and name each quadrilateral.

1. It has two pairs of parallel sides.
   It has no right angles.

   _____

2. All four sides are the same length.
   All angles are right angles.

   _____

3. It has only one pair of parallel sides.
   They are not the same length.

   _____

4. It has two pairs of parallel sides.
   Opposite sides are the same length.
   All angles are right angles.

   _____

Finding Figures within Figures

Malik made this figure on his geoboard. It has squares of different sizes. Count the number of squares it contains.

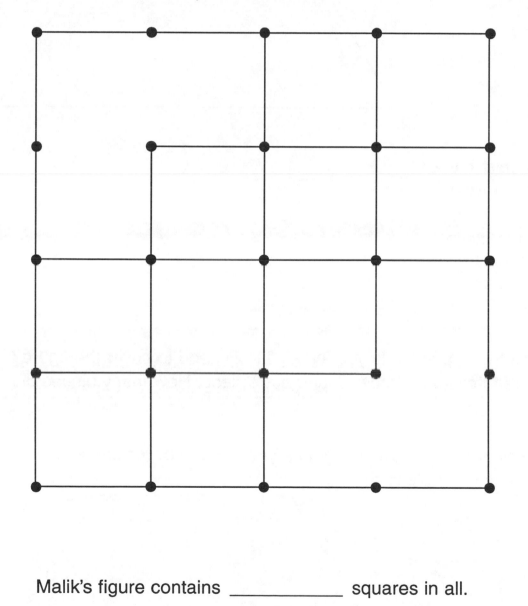

Malik's figure contains _____ squares in all.

TEST

Unit 3 (Analyzing Triangles and Quadrilaterals)

Test 1

1. Name this figure.

_____

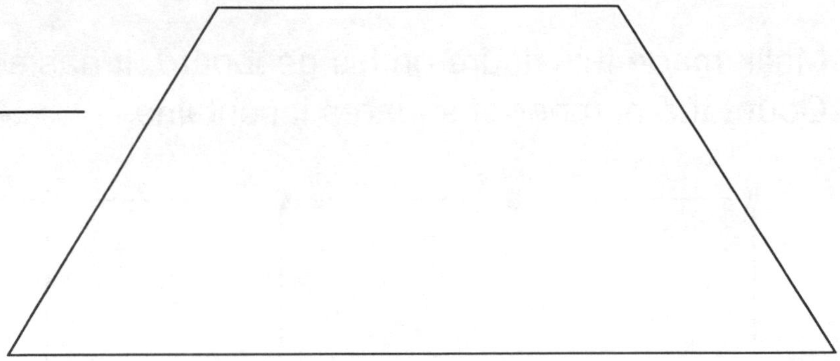

2. The figure above can be covered with several pieces of one type of Power Polygon placed with edges touching. Which piece is it? Sketch it here.

3. How many of these pieces do you think you will need to cover the figure? Use the piece to cover it. Trace around each piece. How many pieces did you use? _____

4. Find other Power Polygon pieces that can be used to cover the figure. Trace and name each piece.

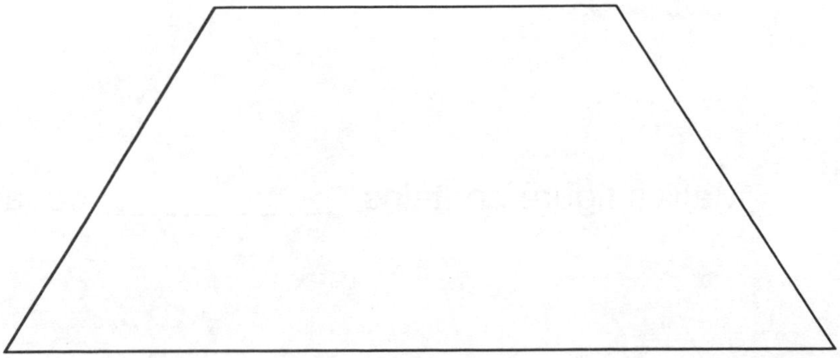

Grade 4
Use after Unit 3.

TEST

Unit 3 (Analyzing Triangles and Quadrilaterals)   Test 2

Examine and compare the polygons. Complete the table.

1. Number of right angles		
2. Number of angles greater than a right angle		
3. Number of angles less than a right angle		
4. Number of sides the same length		
5. Name of polygon		

6. Draw a polygon with four sides that is different from the one above. Name the new polygon. _____

7. Draw a polygon with three sides that is different from the one above. Name it. _____

Name_____ Date _____   ▼ **TEST**

Unit 3 (Analyzing Triangles and Quadrilaterals)   **Test 3**

1. Name each figure.

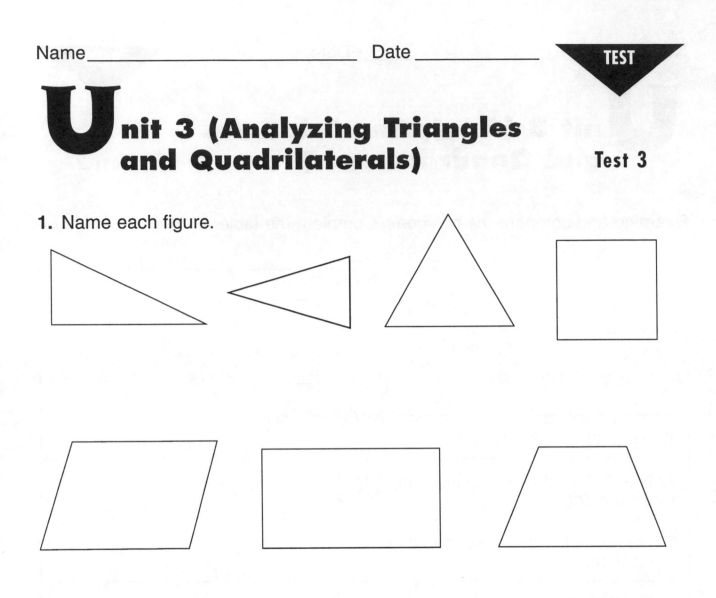

2. Use the names. Sort the figures in the chart.

Contains one or more angles greater than a right angle	Contains all angles less than a right angle	Contains one or more right angles	Has some sides parallel	Has some sides of equal length

34

Grade 4
Use after Unit 3.

Adding

Use mental math. Find each sum.

1. 30 + 26 = _____

2. 25 + 88 + 75 = _____

3. 11 + 65 + 35 = _____

4. 40 + 60 + 34 = _____

5. 250 + 25 + 250 = _____

6. 330 + 84 + 70 = _____

7. 10 + 49 + 390 = _____

8. 49 + 51 = _____

9. 440 + 60 = _____

10. 79 + 420 + 80 = _____

11. 400 + 236 = _____

12. 150 + 150 + 700 = _____

13. 750 + 671 + 250 = _____

14. 85 + 800 + 1200 = _____

15. 660 + 31 + 140 = _____

16. 1000 + 3298 = _____

17. 2500 + 7500 = _____

18. 502 + 700 + 300 = _____

19. 5500 + 384 + 3500 = _____

20. 1320 + 80 = _____

21. 1200 + 4000 + 800 = _____

22. 3000 + 7050 + 50 = _____

23. 40 + 50 + 60 + 31 = _____

24. 500 + 600 + 400 + 520 = _____

25. Check your calculations using a different method.

What method did you use? _____

Name_____ Date _____

ubtracting

Use mental math. Find each difference.

1. 52 – 48 = _____   **2.** 121 – 11 = _____

3. 253 – 23 = _____   **4.** 199 – 16 = _____

5. 82 – 42 = _____   **6.** 92 – 12 = _____

7. 324 – 99 = _____   **8.** 663 – 403 = _____

9. 429 – 97 = _____   **10.** 758 – 204 = _____

11. 298 – 53 = _____   **12.** 355 – 101 = _____

13. 679 – 111 = _____   **14.** 694 – 81 = _____

15. 97 – 49 = _____   **16.** 352 – 47 = _____

17. 810 – 386 = _____   **18.** 219 – 111 = _____

19. 780 – 530 = _____   **20.** 548 – 49 = _____

21. 388 – 284 = _____   **22.** 109 – 10 = _____

23. 228 – 30 = _____   **24.** 950 – 149 = _____

25. Check your calculations using a different method.

What method did you use? _____

Grade 4
Use with Unit 4, Activity 1.

Adding and Subtracting (1)

Find each sum.

1.	37 + 48	**2.**	347 + 82	**3.**	208 + 564	**4.**	687 + 245	**5.**	$8.46 + $7.29

6.	376 + 214	**7.**	734 + 562	**8.**	475 + 538	**9.**	6321 + 2789	**10.**	$68.75 + $94.88

11. 436 + 872 = _____   **12.** 9234 + 398 = _____

13. 286 + 485 = _____   **14.** $73.00 + $42.85 = _____

15. 1762 + 239 = _____   **16.** $7.53 + $28.95 = _____

Find each difference.

17.	914 − 456	**18.**	853 − 386	**19.**	3772 − 1475	**20.**	1683 − 94	**21.**	$5.72 − $1.86

22. 835 − 276 = _____   **23.** 375 − 87 = _____

24. 583 − 95 = _____   **25.** $3.48 − $1.59 = _____

26. $37.75 − $6.35 = _____   **27.** 8751 − 2360 = _____

Adding and Subtracting (2)

These numbers are missing from the calculations in problems 1 to 6.
Use them to complete the calculations.

| 98 | 21 | 99 | 199 | 96 | 52 |

1.
```
   352
 -    
 ─────
   253
```

2.
```
   435
 +    
 ─────
   634
```

3.
```
   151
 +    
 ─────
   249
```

4.
```
   444
 +    
 ─────
   540
```

5.
```
    75
 -    
 ─────
    54
```

6.
```
   1  
 +  48
 ─────
   200
```

Find the missing numbers.

7.
```
   7  
 +  98
 ─────
   820
```

8.
```
   235
 -    
 ─────
   136
```

9.
```
   397
 +    
 ─────
   450
```

10.
```
   5  
 + 198
 ─────
   740
```

11.
```
    64
 +    
 ─────
    83
```

12.
```
   246
 -    
 ─────
   149
```

Grade 4
Use with Unit 4, Activity 2.

Name_____ Date _____

Estimating to Solve Problems

Estimate each solution.

1. Michelle has 376 baseball cards. Tony has 293 baseball cards. About how many more cards does Michelle have than Tony?

_____

2. Stefan and Michelle have the same number of baseball cards. About how many cards do Michelle, Tony, and Stefan have altogether?

_____

3. At the card show, there were 1295 people from Lethbridge, 3363 people from Calgary, and 2642 people from Edmonton. About how many people were there in all?

_____

4. About how many more people were there from Calgary than from Lethbridge at the card show?

_____

5. Suppose 1463 more people came from Red Deer. About how many people would there be in all?

_____

6. Michelle spent $8.27 at the card show. Tony spent $5.81. Stefan spent about twice as much as Tony. About how much money did the three friends spend altogether?

_____

© Addison-Wesley Publishing Company

Using Addition and Subtraction to Solve Problems

1. The Eiffel Tower is 320 m tall. The CN Tower is 555 m tall. How much taller is the CN Tower?

   _____

2. The Eiffel Tower was built in 1889. The Empire State Building was completed 42 years later. In what year was the Empire State Building completed?

   _____

3. Mount Everest is 8848 m tall. How much taller is Mount Everest than the CN Tower?

   _____

4. The Ostankino Tower was completed in 1971. How many years after the Eiffel Tower was built was this?

   _____

5. Suppose it costs $12.00 per adult and $7.95 per child to go to the observation deck of the CN Tower. How much would it cost for two children and an adult?

   _____

6. How many people could visit the CN Tower for $50.00? Give more than one answer if you can.

   _____

   _____

Grade 4
Use with Unit 4, Activity 2.

Estimating Sums and Differences (1)

Use estimation. Which numbers from the box make each sum or difference?
(You can use more than two numbers to make a sum.)

73	126	288	327	406
518	635	757	824	962

1. a sum of about 800 _____

2. a sum of about 1000 _____

3. a sum between 450 and 500 _____

4. a sum close to 685 _____

5. a sum greater than 2000 _____

6. a difference of about 400 _____

7. a difference of about 500 _____

8. a difference between 200 and 300 _____

9. a difference less than 100 _____

10. a difference close to 650 _____

PRACTICE

Estimating Sums and Differences (2)

Estimate each sum or difference.
Use a ✔ mark to show your estimate.

		Less than $10	Between $10 and $20	Greater than $20
1.	$7.22 + $2.86			
2.	$12.04 − $1.95			
3.	$11.87 + $9.68			
4.	$12.91 − $2.99			
5.	$15.25 − $5.94			
6.	$4.06 + $6.40			
7.	$23.01 − $1.95			
8.	$8.86 + $11.86			
9.	$13.47 − $3.65			
10.	$6.19 + $13.40			
11.	$9.95 + $10.22			
12.	$4.45 + $4.95			

Grade 4
Use with Unit 4, Activity 3.

Exploring Multiplication (1)

Write a multiplication sentence. Solve each problem.

1. José bought five packages of juice. There were three juice boxes in each package. How many juice boxes did he buy?

_____

2. Amanda had five candles on her birthday cake. Her mother had six times as many candles on her cake. How many candles did her mother's cake have?

_____

3. Hoy has four coins in his collection. Howin has five times as many coins. How many coins does Howin have?

_____

4. Julie carried two bags of leaves to the curb for collection. She did this four times. How many bags of leaves did she carry in all?

_____

Exploring Multiplication (2)

Find the total value of each set of coins.

1. _____

2. _____

3. _____

4. _____

Continue each skip counting pattern.

5. 0, 4, 8, 12, _____, _____, _____, _____, _____, _____

6. 52, 56, 60, 64, _____, _____, _____, _____

7. 0, 3, 6, 9, _____, _____, _____, _____, _____, _____

8. 30, 33, 36, 39, _____, _____, _____, _____

9. 0, 6, 12, 18, _____, _____, _____, _____, _____

10. 0, 9, 18, 27, _____, _____, _____, _____, _____

Connecting Multiplication and Division (1)

Write a number sentence. Solve each problem.

1. There are two frogs on each pad.
   How many frogs are on three pads?

   _____

2. There are six frogs on three pads.
   The same number of frogs are on each
   pad. How many frogs are on each pad?

   _____

3. There are four socks in each drawer.
   How many socks are in two drawers?

   _____

4. There are eight socks divided equally
   between two drawers. How many
   socks are in each drawer?

   _____

5. There are nine muffins in each pan.
   How many muffins are in two pans?   _____

6. You need eighteen muffins. How many pans
   of nine each do you need?   _____

7. There are seven days in one week.
   How many days are in two weeks?   _____

8. There are fourteen days until school break.
   How many weeks is that?   _____

Connecting Multiplication and Division (2)

Write two multiplication sentences and two division sentences for each situation.

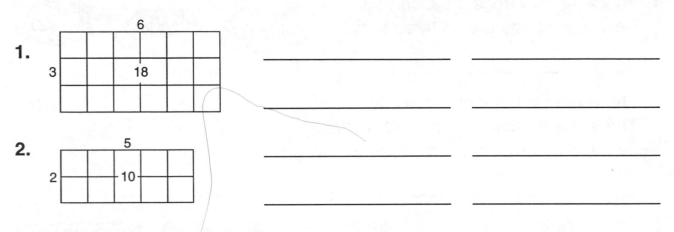

1.

6

3   18

_____   _____

_____   _____

2.

5

2   10

_____   _____

_____   _____

Write three more sentences for each fact family.

3. $7 \times 2 = 14$ **4.** $8 \times 4 = 32$ **5.** $9 \times 2 = 18$

_____   _____   _____

_____   _____   _____

_____   _____   _____

6. $30 \div 6 = 5$ **7.** $24 \div 4 = 6$ **8.** $35 \div 5 = 7$

_____   _____   _____

_____   _____   _____

_____   _____   _____

Grade 4
Use with Unit 4, Activity 5.

Skip Counting

Continue each skip counting pattern.

1. 50, 45, 40, 35, _____, _____, _____, _____, _____, _____

2. 20, 18, 16, 14, _____, _____, _____, _____, _____, _____

3. 30, 28, 26, 24, _____, _____, _____, _____, _____, _____

4. 40, 36, 32, 28, _____, _____, _____, _____, _____, _____

5. 80, 76, 72, 68, _____, _____, _____, _____, _____, _____

6. 80, 72, 64, _____, _____, _____, 32, _____, _____, _____

7. 90, 81, 72, 63, _____, _____, _____, _____, _____, _____

8. 90, 87, _____, 81, _____, _____, 72, _____, _____, _____

9. 30, 27, 24, 21, _____, _____, _____, _____, _____, _____

10. 60, 54, 48, 42, _____, _____, _____, _____, _____, _____

11. 70, 63, _____, _____, 42, 35, _____, _____, _____, _____

Exploring Division

Complete each picture. Write a division sentence.

1. How could you share sixteen crackers equally among four people?

_____

2. You have twelve muffins and three containers. How could you share the muffins equally among the containers?

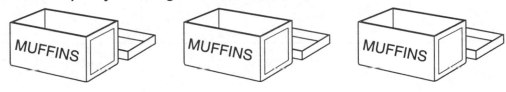

_____

3. How could five children share $45 equally?

_____

4. How many beads could you buy for 25¢?
How much money would be left over?

_____

48

Grade 4
Use with Unit 4, Activity 6.

Multiplying and Dividing (1)

Find each product.

1. $\begin{array}{r} 5 \\ \times 5 \\ \hline \end{array}$	**2.** $\begin{array}{r} 9 \\ \times 5 \\ \hline \end{array}$	**3.** $\begin{array}{r} 8 \\ \times 5 \\ \hline \end{array}$	**4.** $\begin{array}{r} 5 \\ \times 7 \\ \hline \end{array}$	**5.** $\begin{array}{r} 5 \\ \times 3 \\ \hline \end{array}$	**6.** $\begin{array}{r} 5 \\ \times 1 \\ \hline \end{array}$
7. $\begin{array}{r} 3 \\ \times 4 \\ \hline \end{array}$	**8.** $\begin{array}{r} 6 \\ \times 4 \\ \hline \end{array}$	**9.** $\begin{array}{r} 1 \\ \times 4 \\ \hline \end{array}$	**10.** $\begin{array}{r} 9 \\ \times 4 \\ \hline \end{array}$	**11.** $\begin{array}{r} 4 \\ \times 5 \\ \hline \end{array}$	**12.** $\begin{array}{r} 4 \\ \times 4 \\ \hline \end{array}$

13. $4 \times 2 =$ _____   **14.** $2 \times 9 =$ _____   **15.** $7 \times 2 =$ _____

16. $2 \times 6 =$ _____   **17.** $2 \times 8 =$ _____   **18.** $2 \times 5 =$ _____

Find each quotient.

19. $4\overline{)20}$ **20.** $5\overline{)25}$ **21.** $4\overline{)8}$ **22.** $5\overline{)35}$

23. $5\overline{)10}$ **24.** $4\overline{)4}$ **25.** $4\overline{)28}$ **26.** $5\overline{)15}$

27. $4\overline{)32}$ **28.** $5\overline{)30}$ **29.** $5\overline{)5}$ **30.** $4\overline{)12}$

31. $8 \div 2 =$ _____   **32.** $16 \div 2 =$ _____   **33.** $18 \div 2 =$ _____

34. $10 \div 2 =$ _____   **35.** $12 \div 2 =$ _____   **36.** $14 \div 2 =$ _____

37. Write four multiplication or division sentences that have the number 20 in them.

_____ _____ _____ _____

Name_____ Date _____   **PRACTICE**

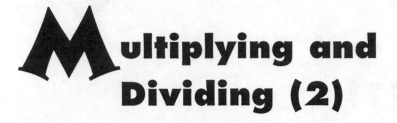ultiplying and
Dividing (2)

Find each product or quotient.

1. 5 ×6	**2.** 5 ×3	**3.** 8 ×6	**4.** 8 ×3	**5.** 6 ×0	**6.** 0 ×3
7. 7 ×3	**8.** 7 ×6	**9.** 2 ×3	**10.** 2 ×6	**11.** 9 ×3	**12.** 9 ×6
13. 1 ×6	**14.** 6 ×2	**15.** 6 ×4	**16.** 6 ×3	**17.** 3 ×4	**18.** 6 ×6

19. $9 \times 3 =$ _____   **20.** $3 \times 2 =$ _____   **21.** $6 \times 5 =$ _____

22. $15 \div 3 =$ _____   **23.** $12 \div 2 =$ _____   **24.** $27 \div 3 =$ _____

25. $6\overline{)12}$ **26.** $3\overline{)12}$ **27.** $6\overline{)6}$ **28.** $6\overline{)24}$

29. $3\overline{)18}$ **30.** $3\overline{)3}$ **31.** $3\overline{)21}$ **32.** $3\overline{)27}$

33. $6\overline{)18}$ **34.** $3\overline{)6}$ **35.** $6\overline{)36}$ **36.** $3\overline{)15}$

37. $6\overline{)48}$ **38.** $6\overline{)30}$ **39.** $3\overline{)27}$ **40.** $6\overline{)42}$

41. Write two multiplication sentences that have a product of 24.

_____   _____

Grade 4
Use with Unit 4, Activity 7.

Multiplying and Dividing (3)

Find each product or quotient.

1. 8 $\times 3$	**2.** 8 $\times 5$	**3.** 4 $\times 8$	**4.** 6 $\times 8$	**5.** 0 $\times 8$	**6.** 8 $\times 2$
7. 7 $\times 8$	**8.** 7 $\times 2$	**9.** 7 $\times 9$	**10.** 7 $\times 6$	**11.** 7 $\times 5$	**12.** 7 $\times 3$

13. $8 \times 7 =$ _____   **14.** $6 \times 7 =$ _____   **15.** $8 \times 8 =$ _____

16. $2 \times 7 =$ _____   **17.** $3 \times 7 =$ _____   **18.** $3 \times 8 =$ _____

19. $9 \times 7 =$ _____   **20.** $8 \times 6 =$ _____   **21.** $8 \times 4 =$ _____

22. $24 \div 8 =$ _____   **23.** $32 \div 8 =$ _____   **24.** $8 \div 8 =$ _____

25. $48 \div 8 =$ _____   **26.** $16 \div 8 =$ _____   **27.** $56 \div 8 =$ _____

28. $21 \div 7 =$ _____   **29.** $63 \div 7 =$ _____   **30.** $49 \div 7 =$ _____

31. $8\overline{)32}$ **32.** $4\overline{)28}$ **33.** $5\overline{)35}$ **34.** $2\overline{)14}$

35. $1\overline{)6}$ **36.** $8\overline{)56}$ **37.** $7\overline{)49}$ **38.** $6\overline{)48}$

Grade 4
Use with Unit 4, Activity 7.

Name_____ Date _____

Multiplying and Dividing (4)

Find each product.

1. $6 \times 4 =$ _____

2. $3 \times 6 =$ _____

3. $6 \times 5 =$ _____

4. $9 \times 8 =$ _____

5. $2 \times 9 =$ _____

6. $3 \times 9 =$ _____

7. $6 \times 7 =$ _____

8. $9 \times 4 =$ _____

9. $6 \times 6 =$ _____

10. $9 \times 5 =$ _____

11. $8 \times 6 =$ _____

12. $6 \times 9 =$ _____

Write a related division fact for each multiplication fact above.

1. _____

2. _____

3. _____

4. _____

5. _____

6. _____

7. _____

8. _____

9. _____

10. _____

11. _____

12. _____

Sort the numbers into the circles.

multiples of 6   multiples of 9

6   12   18   63

24   30   36

42   48   54

60   9   27   45

© Addison-Wesley Publishing Company

Grade 4
Use with Unit 4, Activity 7.

Solving Problems (1)

Solve each problem. Write a number sentence for each problem.

1. Twenty-seven children sign up to play soccer. The coach makes three teams. How many players are on each team?

   _____

2. For a practice drill, the coach divides twenty-one players into groups of three. How many groups can be made?

   _____

3. The coach buys three boxes of sweatbands. There are eight sweatbands in each box. How many sweatbands does she buy?

   _____

4. Rudy and Emily play goalie. Rudy blocks four goals. Emily blocks four times as many goals. How many goals does Emily block?

   _____

5. Thirty-six people go to a swim meet in six cars. Each car holds the same number of people. How many people are in each car?

   _____

6. There are six divers in the swim meet. Each diver makes three dives. How many dives do they make in all?

   _____

7. The pool has six lanes. In a relay, four swimmers race in each lane. How many swimmers are in the race?

   _____

8. Tickets to the swim meet cost $2 each. Marnie has $18. How many tickets can she buy?

   _____

Name_____ Date _____

Solving Problems (2)

Use the menu. Solve the problems.

Hamburger	$2.25	Pizza	$9.00	**Drinks**	
Grilled cheese	$1.50	(extra toppings $0.95 each)		Milkshake	$3.00
Hot dog	$1.30	Pasta	$7.00	Large milk	$1.00
Chicken fingers	$3.00			Small milk	$0.70

1. Chad orders a hamburger, a grilled cheese, and two milkshakes. How much does he pay?

2. Kelly has four loonies, three quarters, one dime, and three nickels. She orders two hot dogs. Does she have enough money left for a drink?

3. The track team orders seven pizzas. What is the total cost?

4. The Ajayi family buys four orders of chicken fingers and four large glasses of milk. How much change will it get from $20?

5. Suppose you have $40. How many orders of pasta can you buy? How much money will you have left over?

6. You have $40. What coins and bills might you have? List at least two combinations.

7. Suppose you share a pizza with two friends. How much will each of you pay?

8. Which costs less: five pizzas or six orders of pasta?

Grade 4
Use with Unit 4, Activity 8.

Unit 4 (Building Operation Sense)

Find each sum.

1. 37 + 48	2. 687 + 245	3. 347 + 82	4. 208 + 564	5. 108 + 693
6. 376 + 214	7. 562 + 734	8. 475 + 538	9. 6321 + 2789	10. $68.75 + $94.88
11. 286 + 485	12. $42.79 + $99.54	13. 681 + 608	14. 926 + 85	15. 4627 + 3895

Find each difference.

16. 53 − 28	17. 38 − 19	18. 443 − 181	19. 632 − 327	20. 212 − 75
21. 345 − 227	22. 723 − 562	23. 464 − 126	24. 6416 − 2075	25. $48.50 − $24.80
26. 855 − 436	27. $8.79 − $2.98	28. 326 − 146	29. 773 − 255	30. 1896 − 968

Unit 4 (Building Operation Sense)

In August, Toys-for-All ordered 602 games, Toys Plus ordered 556 games, and Games Galore ordered 698 games.

1. Which company ordered about 700 games?

_____

2. How many fewer games did Toys Plus order than Toys-for-All?

_____

3. How many more games were ordered by Games Galore than by Toys Plus?

_____

4. How many games were ordered in all?

_____

The Electronic Games Company made 3548 electronic games in May, 3982 in June, and 4083 in July.

5. How many games did the company make in all three months?

_____

6. How many more games were made in July than in May?

_____

7. How many fewer games were made in May than in June?

_____

8. How many more games were made in May and June together than in July?

_____

Grade 4
Use after Unit 4.

Unit 4 (Building Operation Sense)

Test 3

Find each product or quotient.

1. $12 \div 3 =$ _____	**2.** $8 \div 2 =$ _____	**3.** $20 \div 4 =$ _____
4. $6 \div 1 =$ _____	**5.** $64 \div 8 =$ _____	**6.** $30 \div 6 =$ _____
7. $81 \div 9 =$ _____	**8.** $25 \div 5 =$ _____	**9.** $42 \div 7 =$ _____
10. $6 \times 7 =$ _____	**11.** $8 \times 3 =$ _____	**12.** $6 \times 6 =$ _____
13. $9 \times 3 =$ _____	**14.** $6 \times 2 =$ _____	**15.** $3 \times 8 =$ _____
16. $7 \times 4 =$ _____	**17.** $9 \times 9 =$ _____	**18.** $5 \times 5 =$ _____

19. $\begin{array}{r} 4 \\ \times\ 6 \\ \hline \end{array}$	**20.** $\begin{array}{r} 7 \\ \times\ 4 \\ \hline \end{array}$	**21.** $\begin{array}{r} 8 \\ \times\ 8 \\ \hline \end{array}$	**22.** $\begin{array}{r} 8 \\ \times\ 4 \\ \hline \end{array}$
23. $\begin{array}{r} 9 \\ \times\ 5 \\ \hline \end{array}$	**24.** $\begin{array}{r} 3 \\ \times\ 2 \\ \hline \end{array}$	**25.** $\begin{array}{r} 4 \\ \times\ 4 \\ \hline \end{array}$	**26.** $\begin{array}{r} 7 \\ \times\ 7 \\ \hline \end{array}$

27. $7\overline{)56}$	**28.** $9\overline{)36}$	**29.** $9\overline{)63}$	**30.** $6\overline{)24}$
31. $8\overline{)72}$	**32.** $6\overline{)54}$	**33.** $3\overline{)21}$	**34.** $9\overline{)54}$

Complete each number sentence.

35. ___ × ___ = 36	**36.** ___ × ___ = 45	**37.** ___ × ___ = 56
38. $32 \div$ ___ = ___	**39.** $27 \div$ ___ = ___	**40.** $42 \div$ ___ = ___

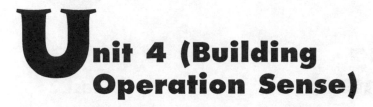nit 4 (Building Operation Sense)

Test 4

Solve each problem.

1. Colin spends five minutes per hour at the computer. How much time will he spend at the computer in a six-hour school day?

_____

2. A set of four computer games costs $36. How much does each computer game cost?

_____

3. Four computers are shared by 32 students. How many students share each computer?

_____

4. Each student spends three hours per week on the computer. How many weeks will it take a student to get 24 hours of computer time?

_____

5. A class pays $36 for six issues of a computer magazine. How much does each issue cost?

_____

6. It takes two minutes to print a copy of Miriam's story. How long would it take to print six copies?

_____

7. The computer disks are stored in boxes of nine. How many disks are in five boxes?

_____

8. How many boxes would be needed to store 60 computer disks?

_____

Grade 4
Use after Unit 4.

Finding Perimeter (1)

Find the perimeter of each figure.

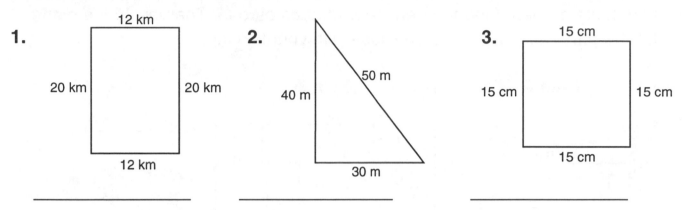

1. 12 km / 20 km / 20 km / 12 km

2. 50 m / 40 m / 30 m

3. 15 cm / 15 cm / 15 cm / 15 cm

_____   _____   _____

Estimate the perimeter of an object like this in your classroom. Use metres.
Check each estimate by measuring.

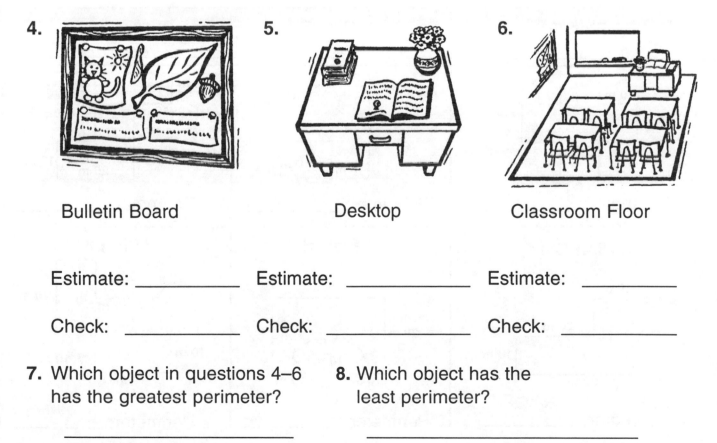

4.   **5.**   **6.**

Bulletin Board   Desktop   Classroom Floor

Estimate: _____   Estimate: _____   Estimate: _____

Check: _____   Check: _____   Check: _____

7. Which object in questions 4–6 has the greatest perimeter?

_____

8. Which object has the least perimeter?

_____

PRACTICE

Finding Perimeter (2)

Suppose you have 100 m of wire fencing. Here are nine different plans for a vegetable garden. Find the perimeter of each garden. Then circle the plans for the gardens that you can enclose with your fencing.

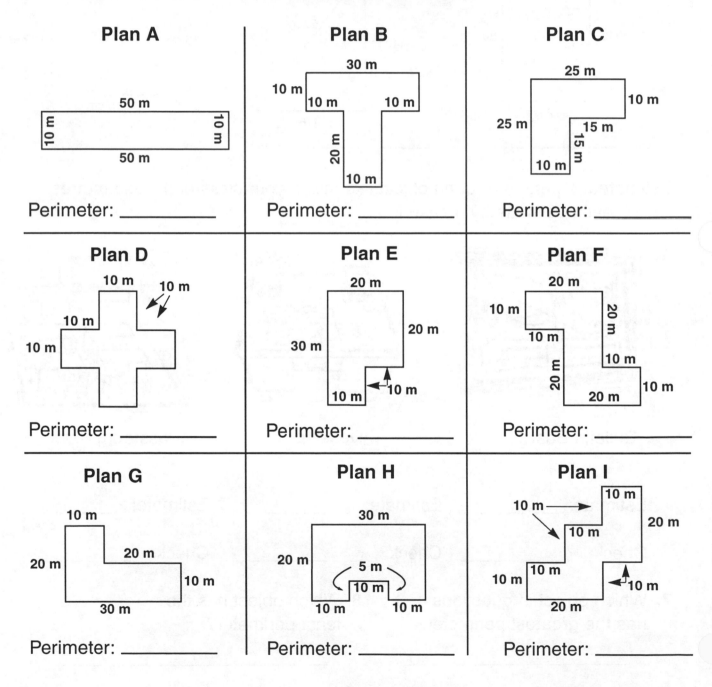

Plan A

50 m
10 m | 10 m
50 m

Perimeter: _____

Plan B

30 m
10 m
10 m | 10 m
20 m
10 m

Perimeter: _____

Plan C

25 m
10 m
25 m
15 m
15 m
10 m

Perimeter: _____

Plan D

10 m
10 m
10 m
10 m

Perimeter: _____

Plan E

20 m
20 m
30 m
10 m | 10 m

Perimeter: _____

Plan F

20 m
10 m
20 m
10 m
10 m
20 m
20 m

Perimeter: _____

Plan G

10 m
20 m
20 m
10 m
30 m

Perimeter: _____

Plan H

30 m
20 m
5 m
10 m
10 m | 10 m

Perimeter: _____

Plan I

10 m
10 m
20 m
10 m
10 m
10 m
10 m
20 m

Perimeter: _____

Grade 4
Use with Unit 5, Activity 1.

Same Area, Different Perimeters

Find the area and perimeter of each figure. On the grid on the right, draw a new figure with the *same* area but a *different* perimeter. Find the perimeter of the new figure.

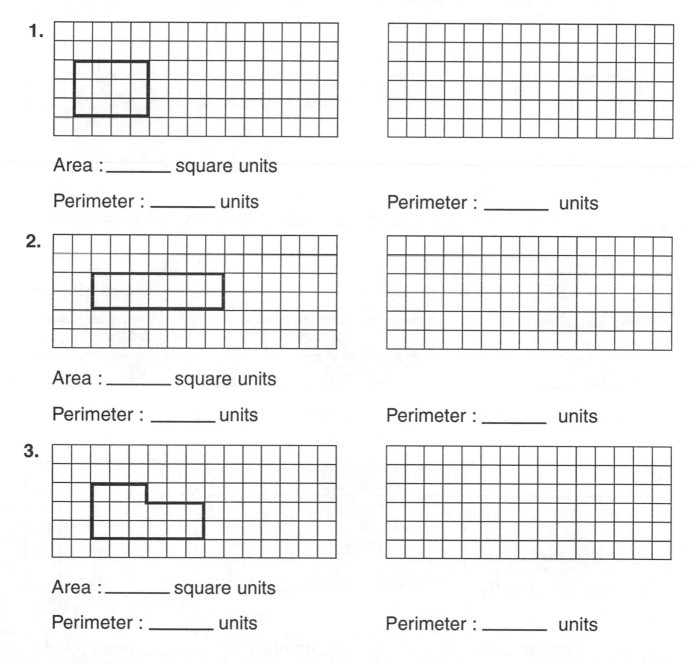

1.

Area : _____ square units

Perimeter : _____ units

Perimeter : _____ units

2.

Area : _____ square units

Perimeter : _____ units

Perimeter : _____ units

3.

Area : _____ square units

Perimeter : _____ units

Perimeter : _____ units

Finding Area (1)

1. 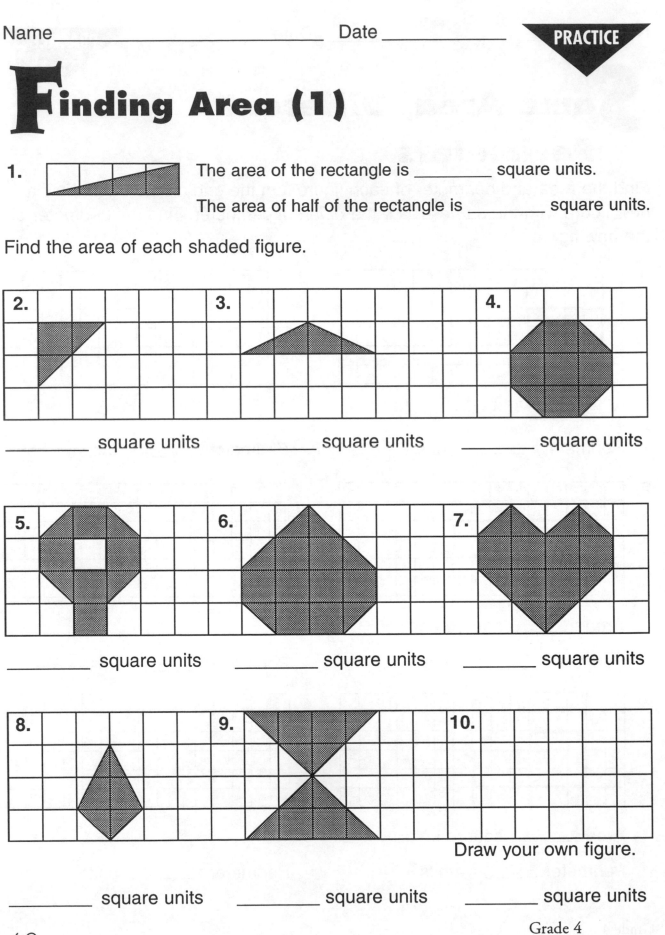 The area of the rectangle is _____ square units.

   The area of half of the rectangle is _____ square units.

Find the area of each shaded figure.

2. _____ square units 3. _____ square units 4. _____ square units

5. _____ square units 6. _____ square units 7. _____ square units

8. _____ square units 9. _____ square units 10. Draw your own figure.

   _____ square units

© Addison-Wesley Publishers Limited

Grade 4
Use with Unit 5, Activity 3.

Finding Area (2)

1. Which figure below do you think has the greatest area? _____

2. Which figure below do you think has the least area? _____

Find the area of each figure in square units.

3.

_____

4.

_____

5.

_____

6.

_____

7.

_____

8.

_____

9.

_____

10.

_____

11.

_____

Name_____ Date _____

Finding the Areas of Right Triangles

Find the area of each triangle in square units.

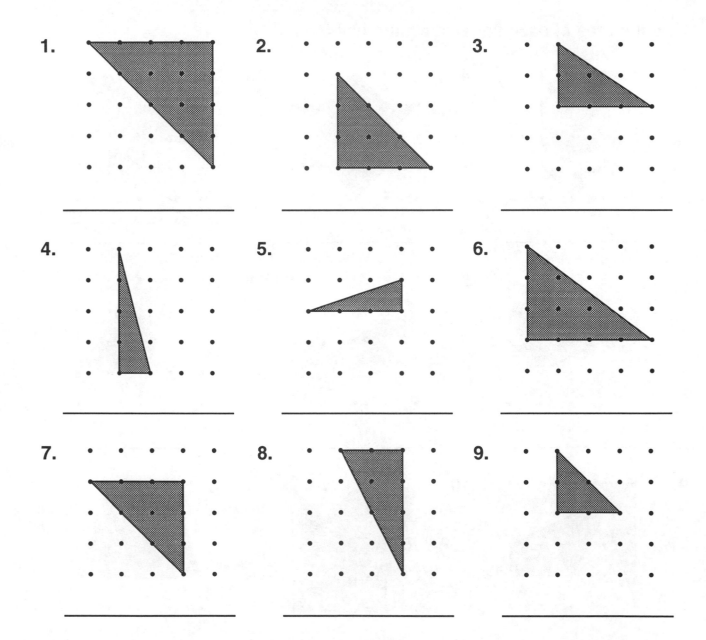

1. _____

2. _____

3. _____

4. _____

5. _____

6. _____

7. _____

8. _____

9. _____

Grade 4
Use with Unit 5, Activity 4.

Finding Area in Square Centimetres (1)

Find the area of each figure in square centimetres.

☐ = one square centimetre

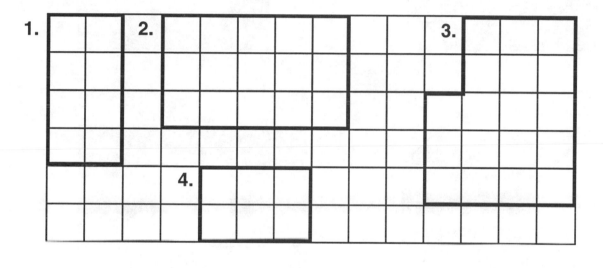

1. _____ 2. _____ 3. _____ 4. _____

Draw a figure for each area given.

5. 9 square centimetres **6.** 11 square centimetres **7.** 20 square centimetres

Finding Area in Square Centimetres (2)

Find the area of each shaded figure.

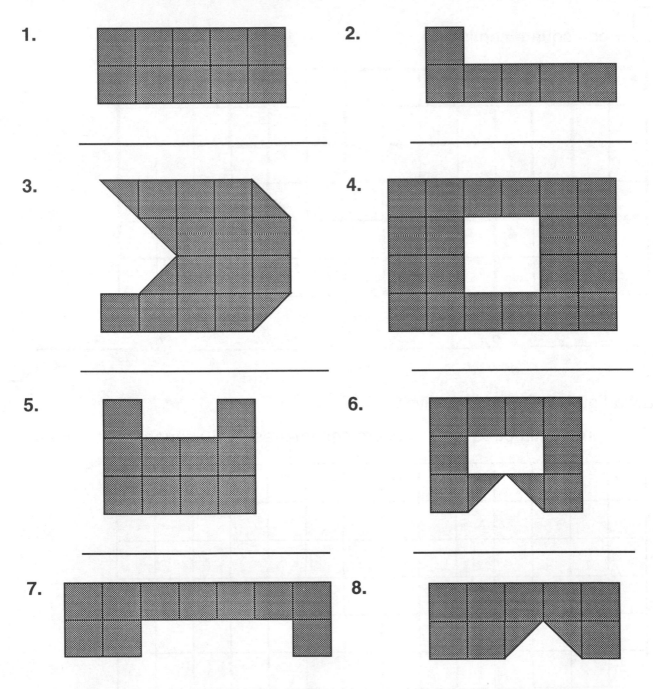

1.

2.

_____

3.

4.

_____

5.

6.

_____

7.

8.

_____

Grade 4
Use with Unit 5, Activity 5.

Name_____ Date _____

Estimating and Measuring Area

Decide whether to use square centimetres or square metres to measure the area of each object.

Estimate each area, then measure to find the area.

Object	Estimated Area	Measured Area
1. a five-dollar bill		
2. a chalkboard		
3. a television screen		
4. a bedroom floor		
5. a tabletop		
6. a book cover		
7. a computer disk		
8. a door		

Unit 5 (Exploring Area and Perimeter)

Test 1

Estimate the perimeter of each figure. Then find the perimeter.

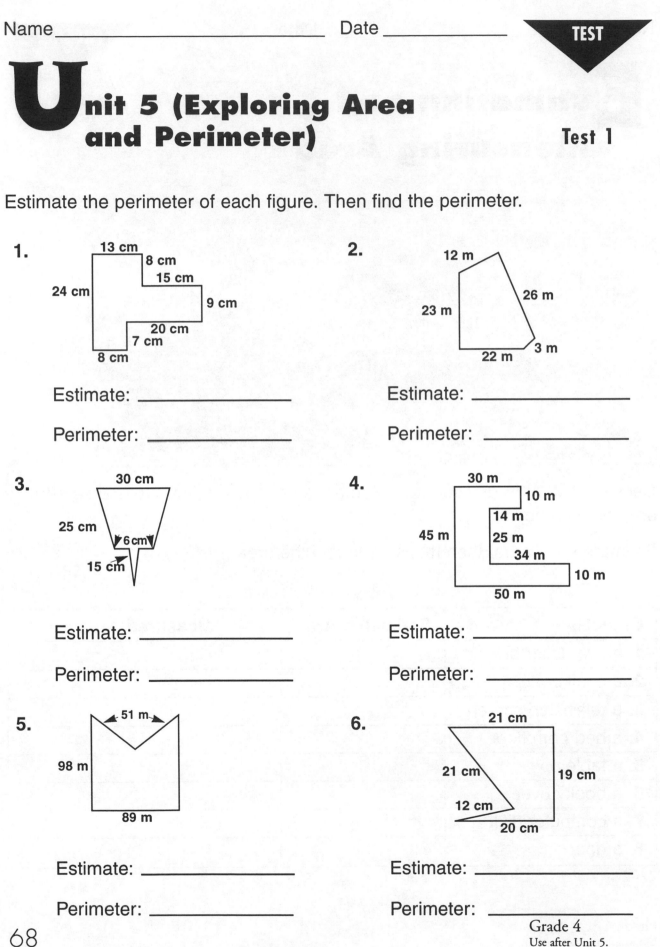

1.
13 cm
8 cm
15 cm
24 cm
9 cm
20 cm
7 cm
8 cm

Estimate: _____

Perimeter: _____

2.
12 m
26 m
23 m
3 m
22 m

Estimate: _____

Perimeter: _____

3.
30 cm
25 cm
6 cm
15 cm

Estimate: _____

Perimeter: _____

4.
30 m
10 m
14 m
45 m
25 m
34 m
10 m
50 m

Estimate: _____

Perimeter: _____

5.
51 m
98 m
89 m

Estimate: _____

Perimeter: _____

6.
21 cm
21 cm
19 cm
12 cm
20 cm

Estimate: _____

Perimeter: _____

Grade 4
Use after Unit 5.

Unit 5 (Exploring Area and Perimeter)

Test 2

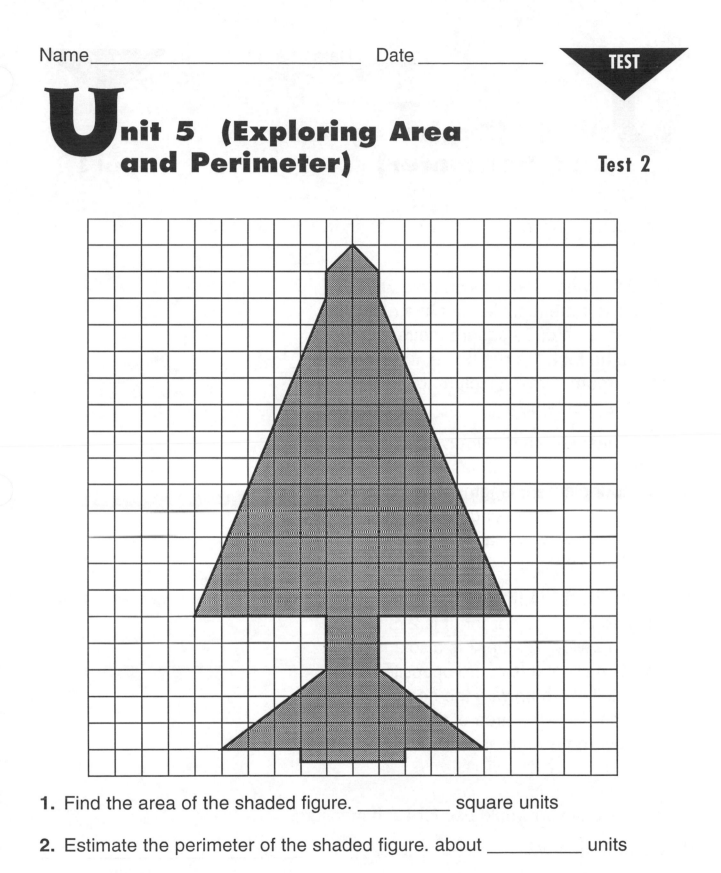

1. Find the area of the shaded figure. _____ square units

2. Estimate the perimeter of the shaded figure. about _____ units

3. Draw a figure with an area of 30 square units on the grid above.

Unit 5 (Exploring Area and Perimeter)

Test 3

Solve each problem. Draw a picture to show each solution.

1. Fredo's living room has an area of 30 square metres. He bought a rug with an area of 30 square metres. When he took the rug home, it did not fit the room. Draw a picture to explain Fredo's problem.

2. Kaye has a strange mirror. Its perimeter is 80 cm. It has six sides with four different lengths. The bottom of the mirror is the longest side. It is 20 cm. Draw what Kaye's mirror might look like. Label its sides.

3. Mike's room is 4 m long and 3 m wide. His bed is in one corner. It is 2 m long and 1 m wide. His desk is also 2 m long and 1 m wide. It is in the opposite corner. Draw Mike's room with the bed and desk in place. Find the area of the floor space *not* covered with furniture.

Name the unit you would use for each measure.

4. the area of a wall _____

5. the area of a photograph _____

6. the perimeter of a photograph _____

Grade 4
Use after Unit 5.

Name_____ Date _____

Exploring Halves

Shade each figure to show one half.

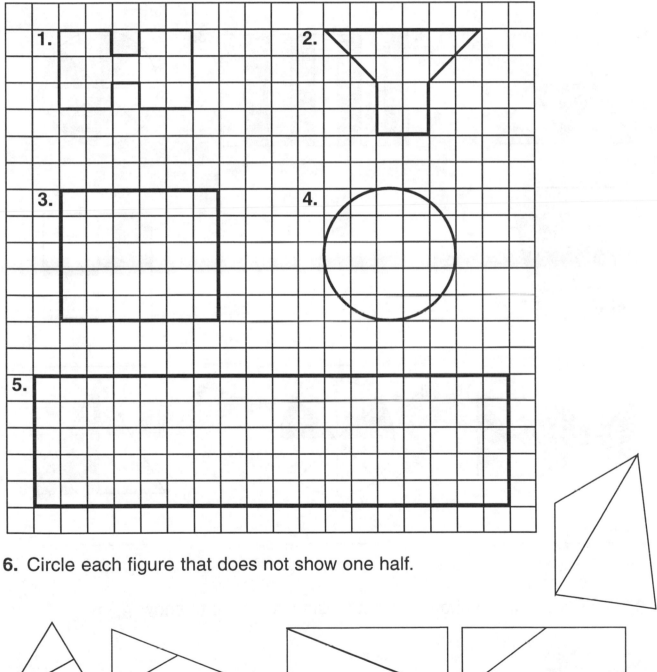

1.

2.

3.

4.

5.

6. Circle each figure that does not show one half.

Naming Fractions

Write a fraction to describe the shaded part of each figure.

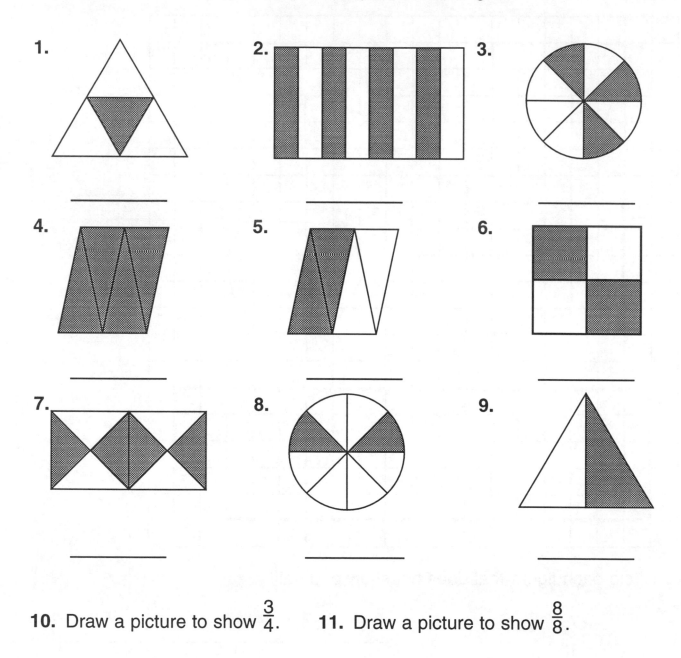

1. _____

2. _____

3. _____

4. _____

5. _____

6. _____

7. _____

8. _____

9. _____

10. Draw a picture to show $\frac{3}{4}$.

11. Draw a picture to show $\frac{8}{8}$.

Grade 4
Use with Unit 6, Activity 1.

Name_____ Date _____

Finding Equivalent Fractions (1)

Complete the equivalent fractions.

1.
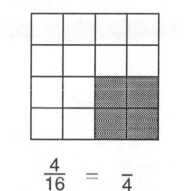

$$\frac{1}{4} = \frac{}{12}$$

2.
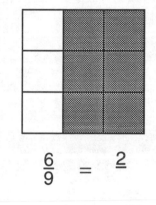

$$\frac{6}{9} = \frac{2}{}$$

3.
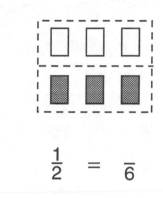

$$\frac{1}{2} = \frac{}{6}$$

4.
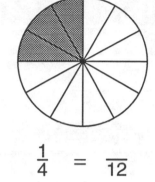

$$\frac{4}{16} = \frac{}{4}$$

5.
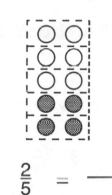

$$\frac{2}{5} = \frac{}{}$$

6.
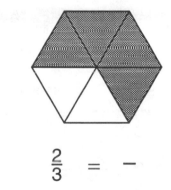

$$\frac{2}{3} = \frac{}{}$$

7.

$$\frac{5}{10} = \frac{}{}$$

8.
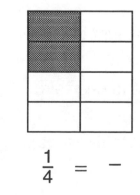

$$\frac{1}{4} = \frac{}{}$$

9.
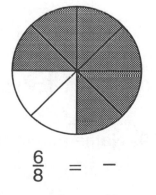

$$\frac{6}{8} = \frac{}{}$$

Finding Equivalent Fractions (2)

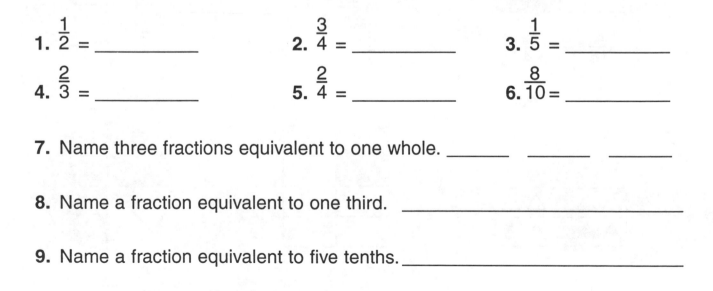

Use the fraction strips. Find an equivalent fraction for each fraction.

1. $\frac{1}{2}$ = _____

2. $\frac{3}{4}$ = _____

3. $\frac{1}{5}$ = _____

4. $\frac{2}{3}$ = _____

5. $\frac{2}{4}$ = _____

6. $\frac{8}{10}$ = _____

7. Name three fractions equivalent to one whole. _____ _____ _____

8. Name a fraction equivalent to one third. _____

9. Name a fraction equivalent to five tenths. _____

Grade 4
Use with Unit 6, Activity 2.

Comparing Fractions (1)

Estimate to answer each question.

1. Is the shaded part greater or less than $\frac{1}{3}$?

_____

2. Is the shaded part greater or less than $\frac{2}{4}$?

_____

3. Is the shaded part greater or less than $\frac{3}{4}$?

_____

4. Is the shaded part greater or less than $\frac{1}{5}$?

_____

Write a fraction for each shaded part.
Circle the greater fraction in each pair.

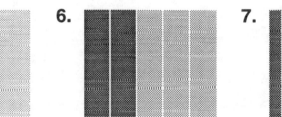

5. ___ ___

6. ___ ___

7. ___ ___

8. Name the greatest fraction shown in the rectangles above. ____

9. Celia and Katie shared a granola bar.

Celia ate $\frac{2}{3}$ of the bar. Katie ate the rest.

Who ate more of the granola bar? _____

Comparing Fractions (2)

Make each statement true by writing < (less than), > (greater than), or = in each ☐. Use fraction circles or strips to help you.

1. $\frac{3}{8}$ ☐ $\frac{4}{8}$

2. $\frac{5}{10}$ ☐ $\frac{7}{10}$

3. $\frac{3}{3}$ ☐ $\frac{2}{3}$

4. $\frac{3}{8}$ ☐ $\frac{1}{2}$

5. $\frac{1}{2}$ ☐ $\frac{1}{4}$

6. $\frac{10}{10}$ ☐ $\frac{5}{5}$

7. $\frac{2}{3}$ ☐ $\frac{4}{5}$

8. $\frac{1}{4}$ ☐ $\frac{2}{8}$

9. $\frac{3}{4}$ ☐ $\frac{5}{12}$

10. $\frac{1}{5}$ ☐ $\frac{1}{4}$

11. $\frac{5}{8}$ ☐ $\frac{2}{3}$

12. $\frac{3}{8}$ ☐ $\frac{1}{4}$

13. $\frac{1}{10}$ ☐ $\frac{1}{5}$

14. $\frac{3}{4}$ ☐ $\frac{2}{3}$

15. $\frac{1}{3}$ ☐ $\frac{4}{6}$

16. $\frac{2}{3}$ ☐ $\frac{3}{8}$

17. $\frac{2}{10}$ ☐ $\frac{1}{5}$

18. $\frac{2}{8}$ ☐ $\frac{3}{4}$

19. $\frac{1}{2}$ ☐ $\frac{1}{3}$

20. $\frac{3}{10}$ ☐ $\frac{1}{4}$

21. $\frac{2}{5}$ ☐ $\frac{3}{10}$

22. $\frac{2}{5}$ ☐ $\frac{3}{4}$

23. $\frac{3}{4}$ ☐ $\frac{5}{8}$

24. $\frac{1}{4}$ ☐ $\frac{1}{10}$

25. $\frac{3}{10}$ ☐ $\frac{1}{5}$

26. $\frac{3}{8}$ ☐ $\frac{2}{5}$

27. $\frac{3}{5}$ ☐ $\frac{3}{4}$

Grade 4
Use with Unit 6, Activity 3.

Naming Fractions of Sets (1)

Write a fraction for the shaded part of each set.

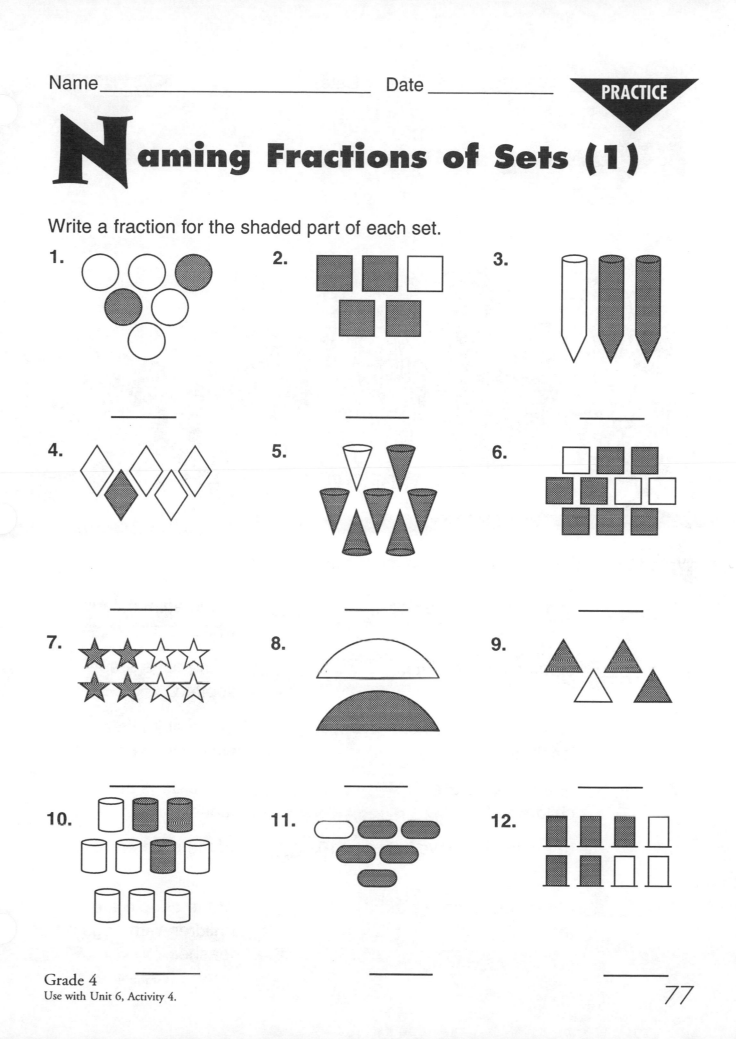

1.

2.

3.

_____

_____

_____

4.

5.

6.

_____

_____

_____

7.

8.

9.

_____

_____

_____

10.

11.

12.

_____

_____

_____

Naming Fractions of Sets (2)

Write the fraction that makes each sentence true.

1. _____ of the animals are dogs.

2. _____ of the animals are white.

3. _____ of the cats are white.

4. _____ of the dogs are spotted.

5. _____ of the animals are on leashes.

6. _____ of the animals are white with short tails.

7. _____ of the people are children.

8. _____ of the dogs are on leashes.

9. _____ of the people have hats.

10. _____ of the children have hats.

11. _____ of the adults have plaid jackets.

12. _____ of the people are children with dogs on leashes.

Grade 4
Use with Unit 6, Activity 5.

Naming Fraction Tenths and Hundredths

Write a fraction for each shaded part.

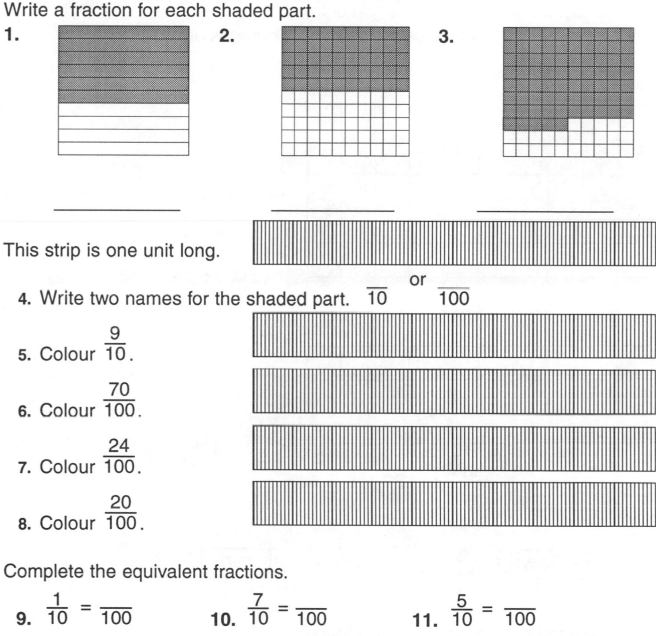

1.

2.

3.

_____   _____   _____

This strip is one unit long.

4. Write two names for the shaded part. $\dfrac{}{10}$ or $\dfrac{}{100}$

5. Colour $\dfrac{9}{10}$.

6. Colour $\dfrac{70}{100}$.

7. Colour $\dfrac{24}{100}$.

8. Colour $\dfrac{20}{100}$.

Complete the equivalent fractions.

9. $\dfrac{1}{10} = \dfrac{}{100}$

10. $\dfrac{7}{10} = \dfrac{}{100}$

11. $\dfrac{5}{10} = \dfrac{}{100}$

Make true statements. Write < (less than), > (greater than), or = in each ☐.

12. $\dfrac{4}{10}$ ☐ $\dfrac{40}{100}$

13. $\dfrac{4}{10}$ ☐ $\dfrac{4}{100}$

14. $\dfrac{4}{10}$ ☐ $\dfrac{35}{100}$

Grade 4
Use with Unit 6, Activity 6.

Showing Tenths and Hundredths

Draw a picture or design on the grid below.
Colour the fraction part indicated for each colour in your picture.

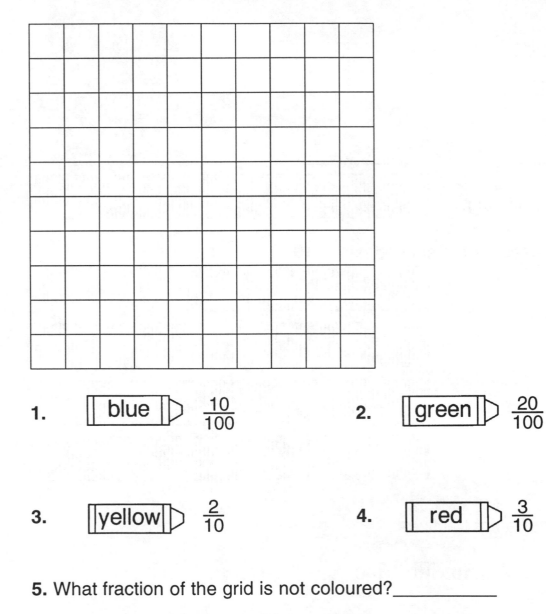

1. | blue | $\frac{10}{100}$

2. | green | $\frac{20}{100}$

3. | yellow | $\frac{2}{10}$

4. | red | $\frac{3}{10}$

5. What fraction of the grid is not coloured?_____

6. What coloured fraction covers the greatest part of the grid?_____

Naming Fractions and Decimals (1)

Write a fraction and a decimal for each shaded part.

	Fraction	Decimal

1. _____ _____

2. _____ _____

3. _____ _____

4. _____ _____

5. _____ _____

Colour your own pattern. Show the colours in the boxes below. Write a fraction and a decimal for each different colour.

	Fraction	Decimal

6. _____ _____

7. _____ _____

8. _____ _____

9. _____ _____

Grade 4
Use with Unit 6, Activity 7.

Name_____ Date_____

Naming Fractions and Decimals (2)

Write a decimal and a fraction for each shaded part.

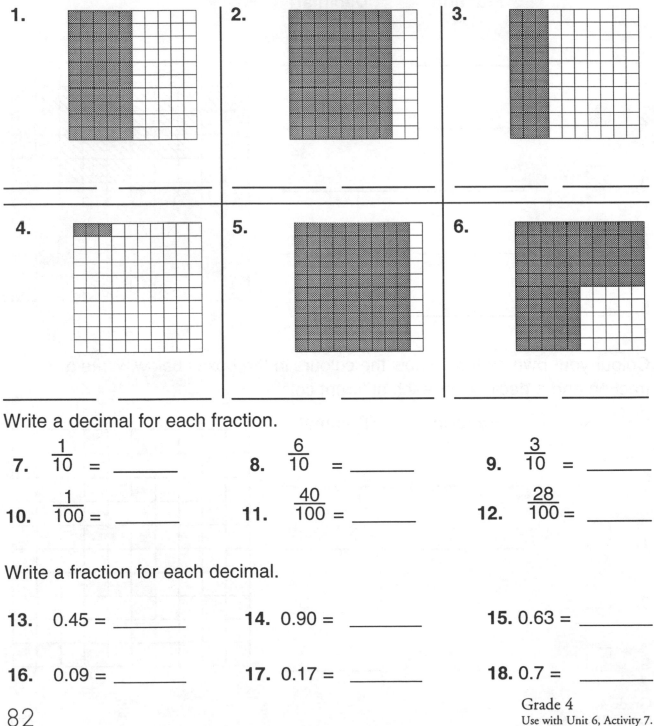

1.

_____ _____

2.

_____ _____

3.

_____ _____

4.

_____ _____

5.

_____ _____

6.

_____ _____

Write a decimal for each fraction.

7. $\dfrac{1}{10}$ = _____

8. $\dfrac{6}{10}$ = _____

9. $\dfrac{3}{10}$ = _____

10. $\dfrac{1}{100}$ = _____

11. $\dfrac{40}{100}$ = _____

12. $\dfrac{28}{100}$ = _____

Write a fraction for each decimal.

13. 0.45 = _____

14. 0.90 = _____

15. 0.63 = _____

16. 0.09 = _____

17. 0.17 = _____

18. 0.7 = _____

82

Grade 4
Use with Unit 6, Activity 7.

Naming Fractions and Decimals (3)

Write a decimal for each shaded part.

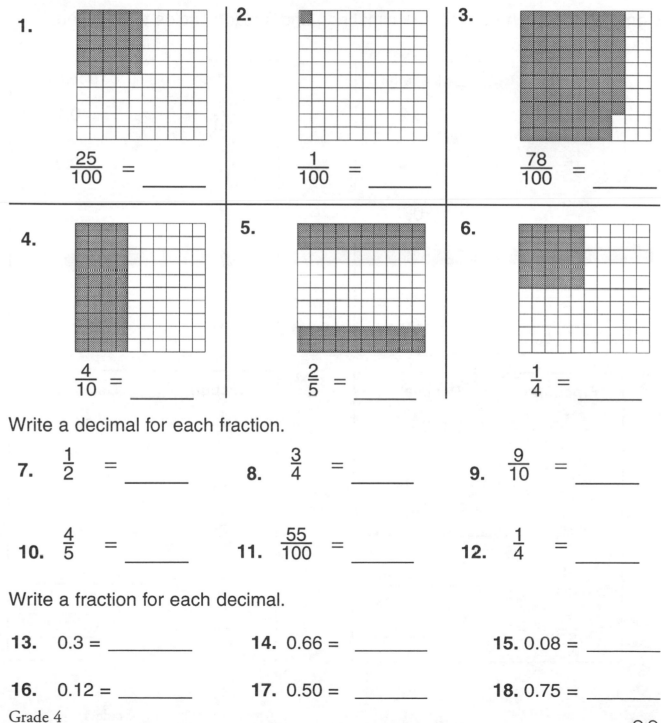

1. $\dfrac{25}{100}$ = _____

2. $\dfrac{1}{100}$ = _____

3. $\dfrac{78}{100}$ = _____

4. $\dfrac{4}{10}$ = _____

5. $\dfrac{2}{5}$ = _____

6. $\dfrac{1}{4}$ = _____

Write a decimal for each fraction.

7. $\dfrac{1}{2}$ = _____

8. $\dfrac{3}{4}$ = _____

9. $\dfrac{9}{10}$ = _____

10. $\dfrac{4}{5}$ = _____

11. $\dfrac{55}{100}$ = _____

12. $\dfrac{1}{4}$ = _____

Write a fraction for each decimal.

13. 0.3 = _____

14. 0.66 = _____

15. 0.08 = _____

16. 0.12 = _____

17. 0.50 = _____

18. 0.75 = _____

Grade 4
Use with Unit 6, Activity 8.

Connecting Fractions and Decimals

Complete each chart. Use a decimal ring and fraction circles to help you.

1.

Fraction		Decimal
$\frac{1}{5}$	=	0.2
$\frac{2}{5}$	=	0.4
$\frac{3}{5}$	=	0.6
$\frac{4}{5}$	=	_____
$\frac{5}{5}$	=	_____

2.

Fraction		Decimal
$\frac{1}{10}$	=	0.1
$\frac{2}{10}$	=	0.2
$\frac{3}{10}$	=	_____
$\frac{4}{10}$	=	_____
$\frac{5}{10}$	=	_____

3.

Fraction		Decimal
$\frac{1}{20}$	=	0.05
$\frac{2}{20}$	=	0.1
$\frac{3}{20}$	=	_____
$\frac{4}{20}$	=	_____
$\frac{5}{20}$	=	_____

4.

Fraction		Decimal
$\frac{1}{25}$	=	0.04
$\frac{2}{25}$	=	0.08
$\frac{3}{25}$	=	0.12
$\frac{4}{25}$	=	_____
$\frac{5}{25}$	=	_____

Grade 4
Use with Unit 6, Activity 8.

Unit 6 (Exploring Fractions and Decimals)

Test 1

Write a fraction for the shaded part of each.

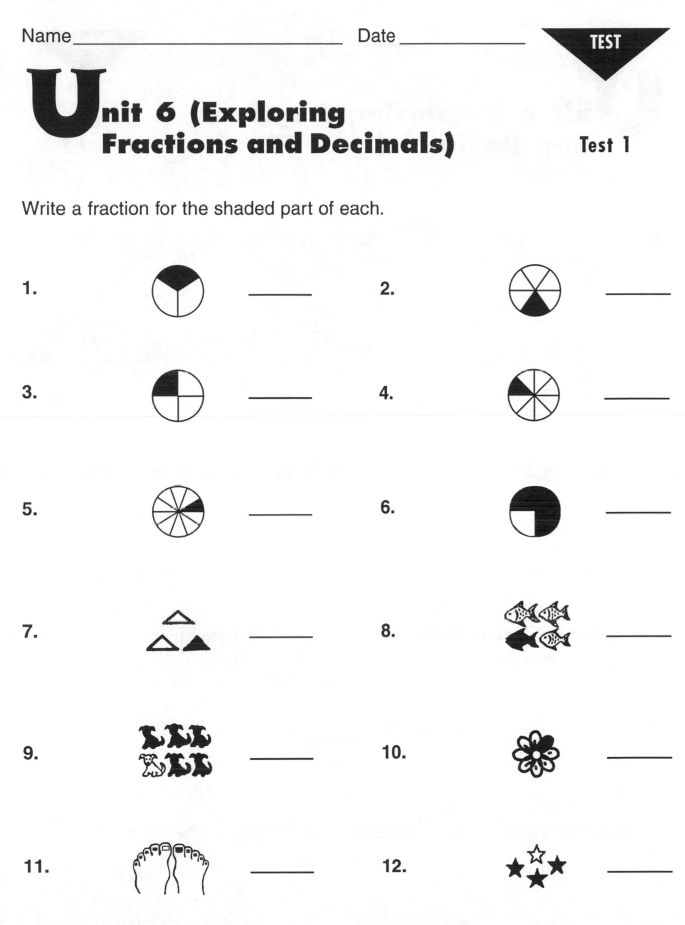

1. _____

2. _____

3. _____

4. _____

5. _____

6. _____

7. _____

8. _____

9. _____

10. _____

11. _____

12. _____

▼ **TEST**

Unit 6 (Exploring Fractions and Decimals)

Test 2

Complete the equivalent fractions.

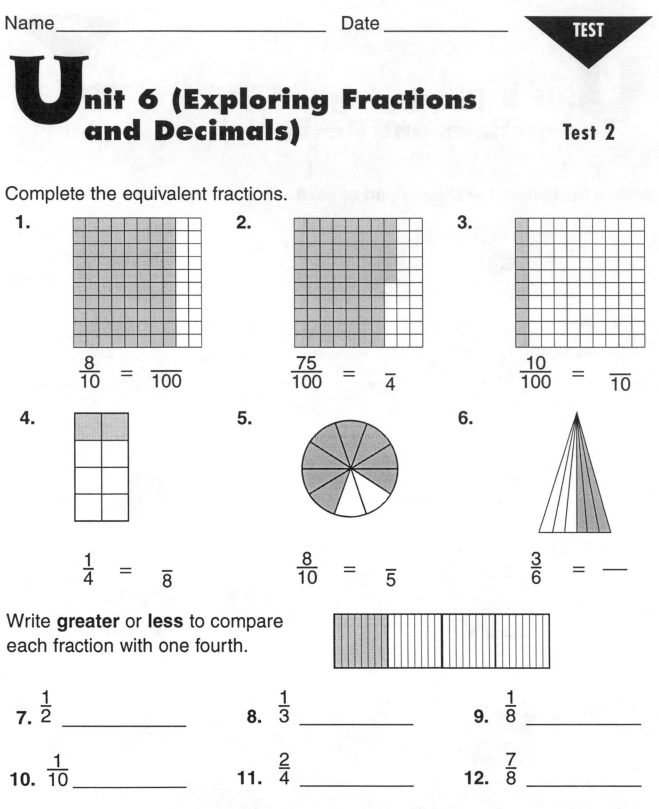

1. $\dfrac{8}{10} = \dfrac{}{100}$

2. $\dfrac{75}{100} = \dfrac{}{4}$

3. $\dfrac{10}{100} = \dfrac{}{10}$

4. $\dfrac{1}{4} = \dfrac{}{8}$

5. $\dfrac{8}{10} = \dfrac{}{5}$

6. $\dfrac{3}{6} = \dfrac{}{\rule{1em}{0.4pt}}$

Write **greater** or **less** to compare each fraction with one fourth.

7. $\dfrac{1}{2}$ _____

8. $\dfrac{1}{3}$ _____

9. $\dfrac{1}{8}$ _____

10. $\dfrac{1}{10}$ _____

11. $\dfrac{2}{4}$ _____

12. $\dfrac{7}{8}$ _____

13. Draw pictures to show that three fourths are greater than one third.

Grade 4
Use after Unit 6.

Unit 6 (Exploring Fractions and Decimals)

Test 3

Write a fraction and a decimal for each shaded part.

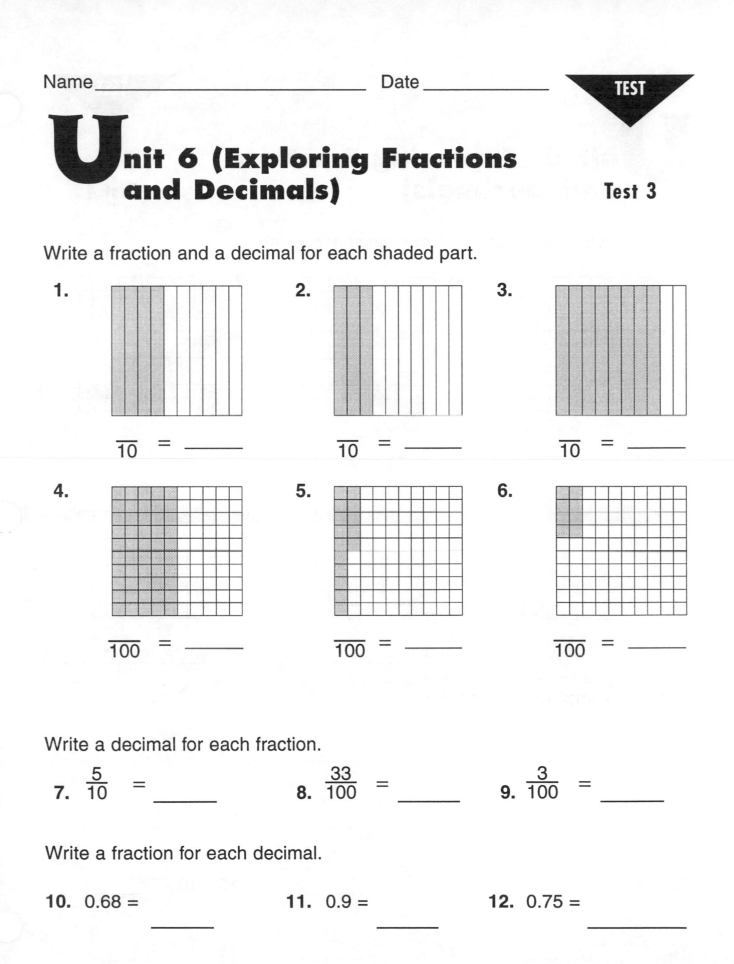

1.

$\overline{10}$ = _____

2.

$\overline{10}$ = _____

3.

$\overline{10}$ = _____

4.

$\overline{100}$ = _____

5.

$\overline{100}$ = _____

6.

$\overline{100}$ = _____

Write a decimal for each fraction.

7. $\dfrac{5}{10}$ = _____

8. $\dfrac{33}{100}$ = _____

9. $\dfrac{3}{100}$ = _____

Write a fraction for each decimal.

10. 0.68 = _____

11. 0.9 = _____

12. 0.75 = _____

Name_____ Date _____

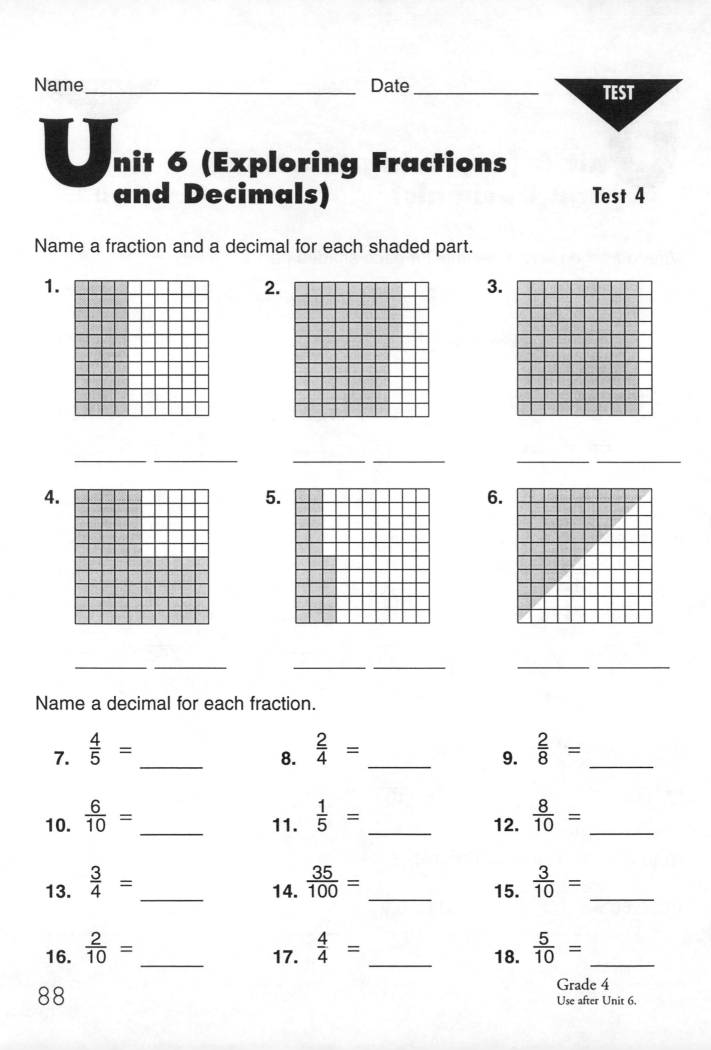

Unit 6 (Exploring Fractions and Decimals)

TEST

Test 4

Name a fraction and a decimal for each shaded part.

1.

_____ _____

2.

_____ _____

3.

_____ _____

4.

_____ _____

5.

_____ _____

6.

_____ _____

Name a decimal for each fraction.

7. $\frac{4}{5}$ = _____

8. $\frac{2}{4}$ = _____

9. $\frac{2}{8}$ = _____

10. $\frac{6}{10}$ = _____

11. $\frac{1}{5}$ = _____

12. $\frac{8}{10}$ = _____

13. $\frac{3}{4}$ = _____

14. $\frac{35}{100}$ = _____

15. $\frac{3}{10}$ = _____

16. $\frac{2}{10}$ = _____

17. $\frac{4}{4}$ = _____

18. $\frac{5}{10}$ = _____

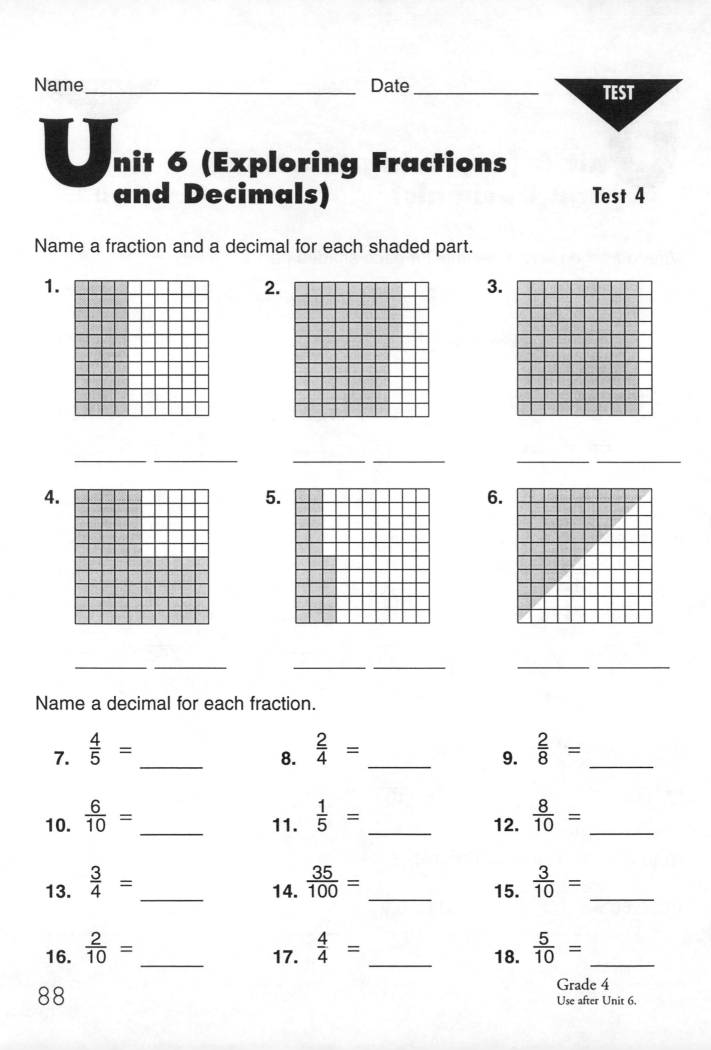

88

Grade 4
Use after Unit 6.

Using Data

Use the bar graph to estimate.

Number of Times You Can Write Your Name in One Minute

Number of Times

1. About how many times could each person write her or his name in two minutes?

   Mikaela: about _____ times   Nathaniel: about _____ times

   Jay: about _____ times   Mary: about _____ times

   Gabriella: about _____ times

2. About how many times could each person write her or his name in five minutes?

   Mikaela: about _____ times   Nathaniel: about _____ times

   Jay: about _____ times   Mary: about _____ times

   Gabriella: about _____ times

3. About how long would it take Mary to write her name 1000 times?   _____

Multiplying by Multiples of Ten

Find each product.

1. 5 × 10 = _____

5 × 20 = _____

5 × 30 = _____

5 × 40 = _____

2. 8 × 10 = _____

8 × 20 = _____

8 × 30 = _____

8 × 40 = _____

3. 3 × 10 = _____

3 × 20 = _____

3 × 30 = _____

3 × 40 = _____

4. 5 × 100 = _____

5 × 200 = _____

5 × 300 = _____

5 × 400 = _____

5. 8 × 100 = _____

8 × 200 = _____

8 × 300 = _____

8 × 400 = _____

6. 3 × 100 = _____

3 × 200 = _____

3 × 300 = _____

3 × 400 = _____

7.   2
$\times$ 10

8.   6
$\times$ 10

9.   4
$\times$ 100

10.   1
$\times$ 100

11. 100
$\times$ 7

12. 10
$\times$ 9

13. 100
$\times$ 3

14. 10
$\times$ 6

Grade 4
Use with Unit 7, Activity 1.

Multiplying Using Arrays (1)

Use grid paper. Draw as many rectangles as you can for each product.
Write a multiplication sentence here for each rectangle you draw.

1. Product: 27
   Multiplication sentences:

2. Product: 29
   Multiplication sentences:

3. Product: 32
   Multiplication sentences:

4. Product: 40
   Multiplication sentences:

5. Draw a different rectangle with the same area as this one.
   Label its length and width.

Name_____ Date _____

Multiplying Using Arrays (2)

Find the area of each rectangle.
Write a multiplication sentence for it.

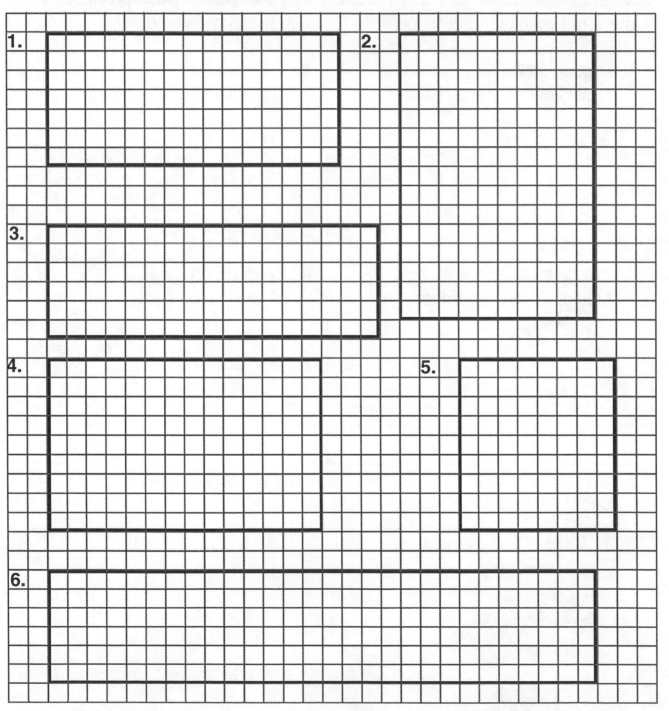

Grade 4
Use with Unit 7, Activity 2.

Using Partial Products

Show how you can separate each product into easier products. Then find each product. The first one is done for you.

1. 25 × 6

20 × 6 = 120
5 × 6 = 30
120 + 30 = 150

Product: __**150**__

2. 36 × 7

Product: _____

3. 8 × 28

Product: _____

4. 31 × 4

Product: _____

5. 150 × 9

Product: _____

6. 103 × 5

Product: _____

7. Draw an array to show 5 × 32. Find the product.

PRACTICE

Multiplying Whole Numbers

Find each product.

| 1. 40
 × 3 | 2. 40
 × 4 | 3. 50
 × 3 | 4. 10
 × 9 |

| 5. 70
 × 3 | 6. 50
 × 5 | 7. 70
 × 6 | 8. 10
 × 8 |

| 9. 20
 × 4 | 10. 30
 × 4 | 11. 50
 × 7 | 12. 10
 × 7 |

| 13. 14
 × 6 | 14. 23
 × 7 | 15. 38
 × 2 | 16. 25
 × 7 |

| 17. 56
 × 8 | 18. 43
 × 7 | 19. 62
 × 8 | 20. 51
 × 1 |

21. $6 \times 32 =$ _____   **22.** $8 \times 73 =$ _____

23. $7 \times 18 =$ _____   **24.** $6 \times 22 =$ _____

25. $9 \times 43 =$ _____   **26.** $5 \times 54 =$ _____

Grade 4
Use with Unit 7, Activity 3.

Using Patterns to Multiply

Find each product.

1. $2 \times 10 =$ _____

2. $6 \times 10 =$ _____

3. $10 \times 4 =$ _____

4. $9 \times 100 =$ _____

5. $3 \times 100 =$ _____

6. $100 \times 7 =$ _____

7. $31 \times 10 =$ _____

8. $48 \times 10 =$ _____

9. $59 \times 10 =$ _____

10. $5 \times 100 =$ _____

11. $8 \times 100 =$ _____

12. $3 \times 100 =$ _____

13. $75 \times 5 = 375$
$75 \times 50 =$ _____

14. $28 \times 2 = 56$
$28 \times 20 =$ _____

15. $39 \times 6 = 234$
$39 \times 60 =$ _____

16. $18 \times 9 = 162$
$18 \times 90 =$ _____

17. $63 \times 4 = 252$
$63 \times 40 =$ _____

18. $24 \times 7 = 168$
$24 \times 70 =$ _____

19. $33 \times 3 =$ _____
$33 \times 30 =$ _____

20. $21 \times 4 =$ _____
$21 \times 40 =$ _____

21. $45 \times 2 =$ _____
$45 \times 20 =$ _____

22. $42 \times 2 =$ _____
$42 \times 20 =$ _____

23. $25 \times 5 =$ _____
$25 \times 50 =$ _____

24. $51 \times 3 =$ _____
$51 \times 30 =$ _____

Grade 4
Use with Unit 7, Activity 4.

Problem Solving (1)

Josie and her dad decided to build a bookcase. First they drew a plan of what the bookcase will look like. Use the drawing to answer each question. Write a multiplication sentence for each.

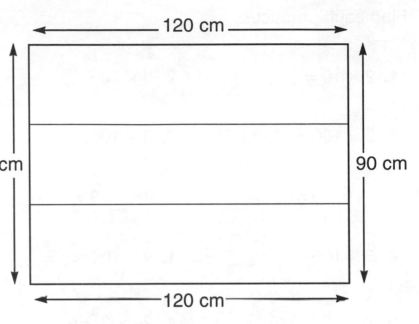

1. Josie and her dad will buy one long board. It will be cut for the two sides of the bookcase. What length board will they need to buy?

_____

2. Josie and her dad will buy another board. It will be cut for the shelves and the top and bottom of the bookcase. What length board will they need to buy?

_____

3. They need four screws for each shelf and side. How many screws do they need altogether?

_____

4. Josie can put 40 books on each shelf. How many books can she put in her bookcase?

_____

5. It took Josie's dad 50 minutes to cut the boards, sand them, and screw them together. It took Josie three times as long to paint the bookcase. How long did it take her to paint the bookcase?

_____

Grade 4
Use with Unit 7, Activity 4.

Name_____ Date _____

Estimating Products (1)

Estimate whether each product is less than 100,
between 100 and 200, or greater than 200.
Put a ✔ in the correct column.

	Less than 100	Between 100 and 200	Greater than 200
1. 36 × 3			
2. 18 × 4			
3. 47 × 6			
4. 34 × 5			
5. 62 × 4			
6. 32 × 3			
7. 76 × 2			
8. 42 × 5			
9. 57 × 3			
10. 17 × 7			
11. 75 × 3			
12. 12 × 20			
13. 27 × 8			
14. 53 × 2			
15. 29 × 6			

Grade 4
Use with Unit 7, Activity 5.

97

Estimating Products (2)

Pick one factor from each bowl to form each product. Use estimation.
Write a multiplication sentence for each product.

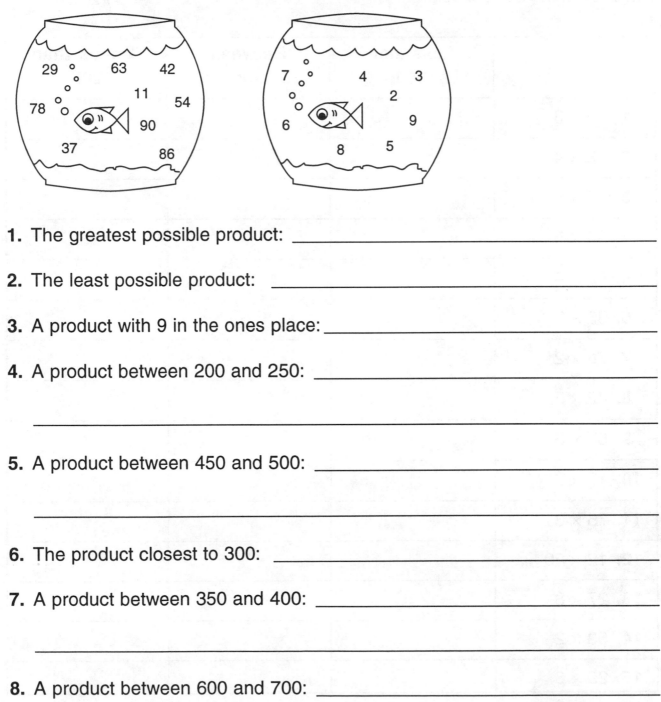

1. The greatest possible product: _____

2. The least possible product: _____

3. A product with 9 in the ones place: _____

4. A product between 200 and 250: _____

_____

5. A product between 450 and 500: _____

_____

6. The product closest to 300: _____

7. A product between 350 and 400: _____

_____

8. A product between 600 and 700: _____

98

PRACTICE

ultiplying (1)

Find each product.

1. 23	2. 18	3. 35	4. 26
× 4	× 3	× 2	× 5

5. 21	6. 16	7. 16	8. 52
× 4	× 3	× 4	× 3

9. 63	10. 42	11. 32	12. 13
× 7	× 5	× 6	× 9

13. 44	14. 74	15. 82	16. 39
× 6	× 2	× 5	× 4

17. 43	18. 68	19. 95	20. 56
× 7	× 3	× 8	× 6

21. 55	22. 76	23. 63	24. 87
× 5	× 4	× 7	× 3

ultiplying (2)

Find each product.

1.	198 × 2	**2.**	958 × 4	**3.**	426 × 5	**4.**	583 × 6

5.	395 × 3	**6.**	978 × 2	**7.**	614 × 3	**8.**	354 × 4

9.	126 × 9	**10.**	349 × 5	**11.**	283 × 8	**12.**	695 × 6

13.	344 × 7	**14.**	746 × 4	**15.**	376 × 2	**16.**	626 × 5

17.	328 × 7	**18.**	632 × 5	**19.**	732 × 8	**20.**	536 × 5

21. Check your solutions. Describe the strategy you used.

_____

Name_____ Date _____

Dividing Using Arrays

The table gives the numbers of square tiles from which rectangles will be made. It also gives the number of rows each rectangle will have. Find the greatest number of columns each rectangle can have. Record the number of leftover tiles, if any. Write a number sentence for the area of each completed rectangle.

	Number of tiles	Number of rows in rectangle	Number of columns in rectangle	Number of leftover tiles	Number sentence for area of completed rectangle
1.	75	2			
2.	26	6			
3.	56	3			
4.	33	11			
5.	26	3			
6.	95	8			
7.	82	7			
8.	36	5			
9.	31	6			

10. Alan has 90 tiles. He plans to use all of them to make a rectangle. Write number sentences for the different sizes the rectangle could be.

_____

_____

Dividing Whole Numbers

Find each quotient and remainder.

1. 7)40   **2.** 6)26   **3.** 8)75

4. 4)25   **5.** 7)24   **6.** 9)56

7. 6)37   **8.** 7)56   **9.** 8)63

10. 5)42   **11.** 5)29   **12.** 9)47

13. 6)48   **14.** 8)35   **15.** 7)50

16. Check your solutions. Describe the strategy you used.

_____

Grade 4
Use with Unit 7, Activity 7.

Problem Solving (2)

Solve. Think about how to interpret the remainder.

1. Socks are $4 a pair. Ben has $14 to buy socks. How many pairs can he buy?

_____

2. Ninety-eight people are going on a tour. They will be in groups of five. How many groups wil there be?

_____

3. Andie is to put 70 glasses in boxes. Only 8 glasses will fit in one box. How many boxes does she need?

_____

4. A recipe calls for three bananas to make one loaf of banana bread. How many loaves can be made from four dozen bananas?

_____

5. There are 86 people who want to be on baseball teams. There are 9 people on a team. How many teams can they make?

_____

6. Linda has $26. One tape costs $8. How many tapes can Linda buy?

_____

7. The 75 members of a ski club want to take a trip. Each car can carry 6 members. How many cars do they need?

_____

8. Juice is to be served to 20 people. The juice comes in packages of 6 servings. How many packages are needed?

_____

Name_____ Date _____

Problem Solving (3)

1. There are 27 campers. Grape drink comes in six-packs and orange drink comes in four-packs. How many six-packs and how many four-packs should you buy to have the fewest drinks left over?

You want some of each kind of drink.

Number of six-packs	Number of four-packs	Total number of drinks	Number of drinks left over
3	3	18 + 12 = 30	3

2. There are 29 campers. Joe needs groups of exactly six campers for his activity. Sherry needs groups of exactly seven for hers. How can you group campers so that there are the fewest campers left over?

Each counsellor must have at least one group.

Number of groups of 6	Number of groups of 7	Total number of campers in groups	Number of campers left over

Dividing (1)

Find each quotient.

1. 36 ÷ 6 = _____

2. 48 ÷ 8 = _____

3. 81 ÷ 9 = _____

4. 75 ÷ 8 = _____

5. 31 ÷ 5 = _____

6. 48 ÷ 9 = _____

7. 12 ÷ 8 = _____

8. 24 ÷ 7 = _____

9. 27 ÷ 4 = _____

10. 15 ÷ 2 = _____

11. 15 ÷ 3 = _____

12. 16 ÷ 5 = _____

13. 56 ÷ 9 = _____

14. 63 ÷ 9 = _____

15. 63 ÷ 8 = _____

16. 41 ÷ 5 = _____

17. 25 ÷ 3 = _____

18. 45 ÷ 7 = _____

19. 35 ÷ 3 = _____

20. 69 ÷ 7 = _____

21. 50 ÷ 2 = _____

22. 48 ÷ 5 = _____

23. 34 ÷ 6 = _____

24. 50 ÷ 8 = _____

25. 30 ÷ 8 = _____

26. 39 ÷ 4 = _____

27. 52 ÷ 6 = _____

Dividing (2)

Find each quotient.

1. $5\overline{)75}$ **2.** $4\overline{)80}$ **3.** $7\overline{)97}$

4. $3\overline{)79}$ **5.** $9\overline{)87}$ **6.** $5\overline{)80}$

7. $8\overline{)61}$ **8.** $3\overline{)80}$ **9.** $4\overline{)49}$

10. $6\overline{)47}$ **11.** $6\overline{)84}$ **12.** $3\overline{)29}$

13. $7\overline{)50}$ **14.** $2\overline{)81}$ **15.** $8\overline{)77}$

16. Check your solutions. Describe the strategy you used.

_____

_____

_____

Unit 7 (Understanding Multiplication and Division)   Test 1

Colour an array to represent each expression. Then find the product.

1. $4 \times 17 =$ _____

2. $6 \times 19 =$ _____

Write a multiplication sentence to show the shaded area in square units for each array.

3. _____

4. _____

Write a division sentence for each array.

5. An array has 75 square units. It has 5 rows. How many columns does it have?

6. An array has 96 square units. It has 8 rows. How many columns does it have?

_____

_____

Unit 7 (Understanding Multiplication and Division) Test 2

Estimate each product.

1. $7 \times 43 =$ about _____

2. $4 \times 38 =$ about _____

3. $\$53 \times 8 =$ about _____

4. $69 \times 5 =$ about _____

5. $9 \times 67 =$ about _____

6. $3 \times 18 =$ about _____

7. $6 \times \$4.92 =$ about _____

8. $268 \times 5 =$ about _____

9. $9 \times 295 =$ about _____

10. $8 \times 31 =$ about _____

11. $29 \times 3 =$ about _____

12. $39 \times 4 =$ about _____

13. $463 \times 9 =$ about _____

14. $53 \times 6 =$ about _____

Estimate whether each product is greater or less than 1000. Write **greater** or **less**.

15. 5×198 _____

16. 4×285 _____

17. 2×449 _____

18. 8×117 _____

19. 190×6 _____

20. 3×425 _____

21. 36×20 _____

22. 28×30 _____

23. 41×30 _____

24. 42×20 _____

Grade 4
Use after Unit 7.

Unit 7 (Understanding Multiplication and Division) Test 3

Find each product.

1. $2 \times 10 =$ _____   **2.** $6 \times 10 =$ _____   **3.** $10 \times 4 =$ _____

4. $9 \times 100 =$ _____   **5.** $3 \times 100 =$ _____   **6.** $100 \times 7 =$ _____

7.
$$\begin{array}{r} 14 \\ \times\ 3 \\ \hline \end{array}$$

8.
$$\begin{array}{r} 27 \\ \times\ 4 \\ \hline \end{array}$$

9.
$$\begin{array}{r} 32 \\ \times\ 5 \\ \hline \end{array}$$

10.
$$\begin{array}{r} 25 \\ \times\ 6 \\ \hline \end{array}$$

11.
$$\begin{array}{r} 162 \\ \times\ 5 \\ \hline \end{array}$$

12.
$$\begin{array}{r} 434 \\ \times\ 2 \\ \hline \end{array}$$

13.
$$\begin{array}{r} 152 \\ \times\ 6 \\ \hline \end{array}$$

14.
$$\begin{array}{r} 238 \\ \times\ 9 \\ \hline \end{array}$$

15. Describe how to check your solutions to multiplication problems.

_____

Find each quotient.

16. $56 \div 9 =$ _____   **17.** $63 \div 9 =$ _____   **18.** $62 \div 8 =$ _____

19. $41 \div 5 =$ _____   **20.** $25 \div 3 =$ _____   **21.** $45 \div 7 =$ _____

22. $8\overline{)98}$ **23.** $4\overline{)57}$ **24.** $3\overline{)54}$

25. $5\overline{)79}$ **26.** $2\overline{)36}$ **27.** $9\overline{)99}$

28. Describe how to check your solutions to division problems.

_____

Grade 4
Use after Unit 7.

Unit 7 (Understanding Multiplication and Division)   Test 4

Solve each problem. Write a number sentence for each.

1. A safari train can carry 96 passengers. Each car holds 8 people. How many cars does the train have?

_____

2. The train in problem 1 has 6 windows in each car. How many windows does it have?

_____

3. There are 28 posters for sale at each of 3 train stops. How many posters are there altogether?

_____

4. The safari train travels 7 m in one second. At this speed, about how long would it take to travel 50 m?

_____

Make up a story problem.

5. A problem that can be solved by multiplying 128 by 6.

_____

_____

_____

6. A problem that can be solved by dividing 80 by 5.

_____

_____

_____

Identifying Lines

1. Circle the sets of lines that are parallel.

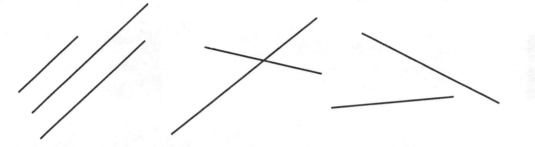

2. Circle the sets of lines that are intersecting and perpendicular.

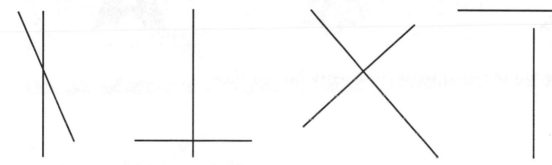

3. Draw a picture that includes horizontal lines, vertical lines, parallel lines, and perpendicular lines. Label each line or set of lines.

Identifying Symmetry

Draw a line of symmetry for each picture.

1. **M**

2.

3. **E**

4. **X**

5.

6. **A**

Complete each drawing to make a symmetrical figure.
Draw lines of symmetry.

7.

8.

9.

10. Draw a symmetrical figure.

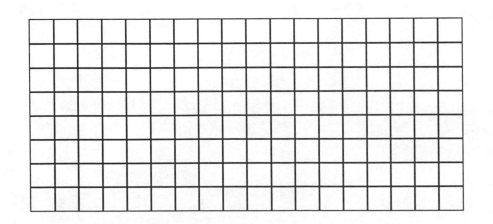

Grade 4
Use with Unit 8, Activity 1.

Comparing Geometric Solids

Write **pyramid** or **prism** to name each solid.

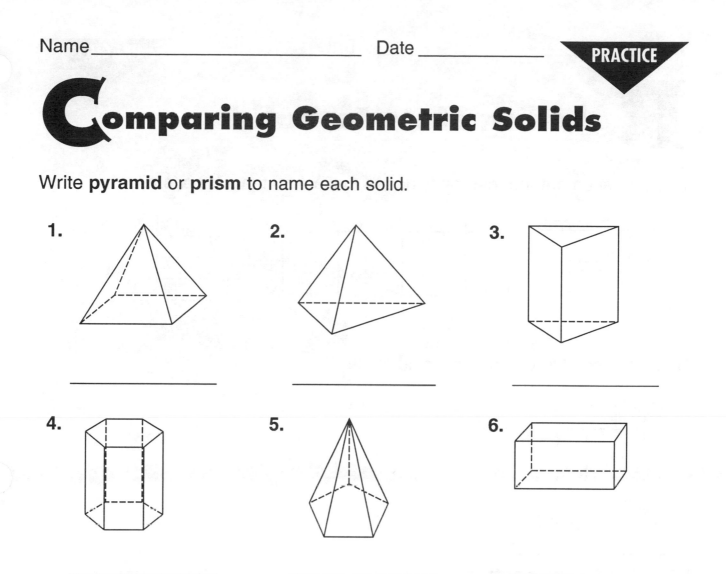

1.

_____

2.

_____

3.

_____

4.

_____

5.

_____

6.

_____

Draw a line to match each riddle with the name of a solid.

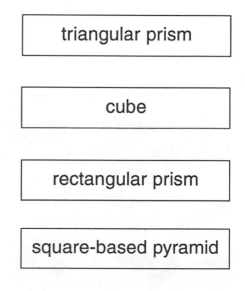

7. I have two square faces that are horizontal.
   I have four vertical faces that are square.

8. None of my five faces is parallel to any
   other face. One of my faces is square.

9. I have three pairs of parallel faces.
   All six faces are rectangles.

10. I have five faces. My two triangular faces
   are parallel.

triangular prism

cube

rectangular prism

square-based pyramid

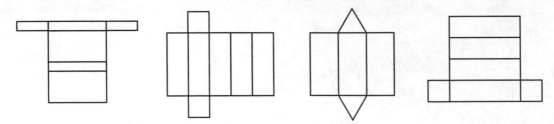

Relating Nets to Solids

1. Circle each net that can be folded to make a rectangular prism.

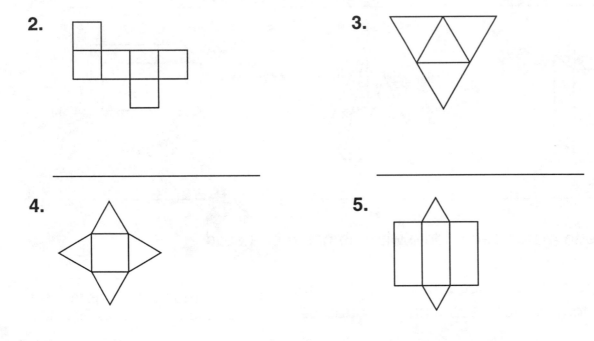

Name the solid that each net could make.

2.

_____

3.

_____

4.

_____

5.

_____

6. Draw a net for a pentagonal pyramid.

Grade 4
Use with Unit 8, Activity 2.

Identifying Quadrilaterals

1. Circle each quadrilateral.

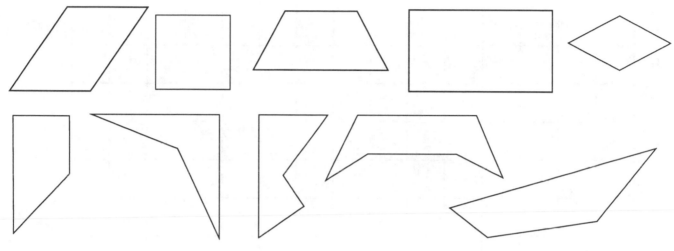

2. Complete the chart.

Figure	Number of pairs of parallel sides	Number of square vertices	Number of sides of equal length
square			
rectangle			
parallelogram			
rhombus			
trapezoid			

Locating Figures on a Grid

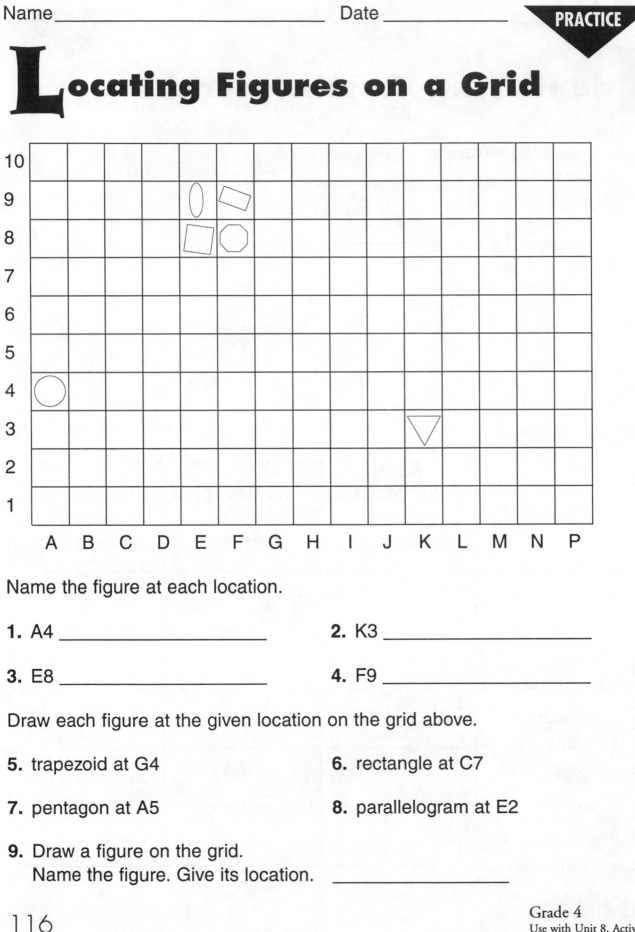

Name the figure at each location.

1. A4 _____

2. K3 _____

3. E8 _____

4. F9 _____

Draw each figure at the given location on the grid above.

5. trapezoid at G4

6. rectangle at C7

7. pentagon at A5

8. parallelogram at E2

9. Draw a figure on the grid.
Name the figure. Give its location. _____

Grade 4
Use with Unit 8, Activity 3.

Using Maps

Describe each location as **north**, **south**, **east**, or **west** of the school on the map.

1. A _____   **2.** B _____   **3.** C _____

Describe how to get from one location to another.
Use the terms **north, south, east,** and **west.**

4. A to D _____

_____

5. C to A to B _____

_____

6. Mark a location on the map that is west of A. Describe how to get from the new location to B, stopping at C on the way.

_____

_____

© Addison-Wesley Publishers Limited

Unit 8 (Placing Figures in Space)

Test 1

Use the term **parallel, intersecting,** or **perpendicular.**
Describe each set of lines.

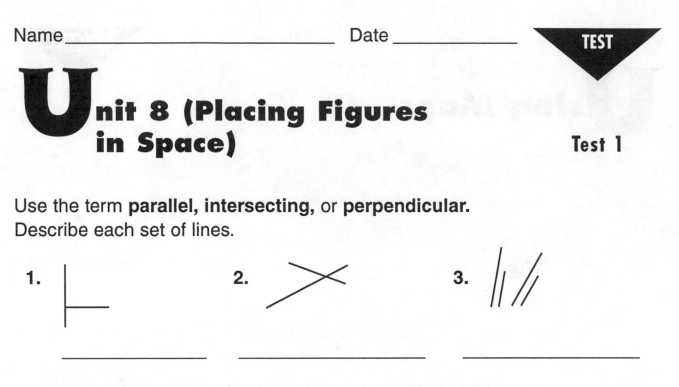

1. _____

2. _____

3. _____

4. Circle the figure if the line across it is a line of symmetry.

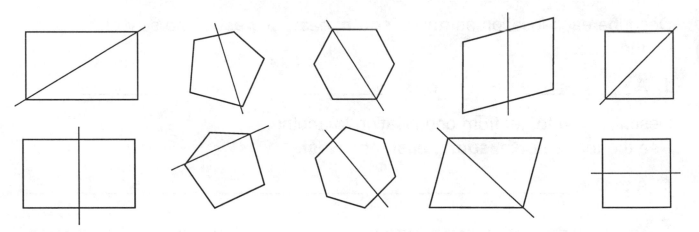

Draw lines of symmetry, if possible.

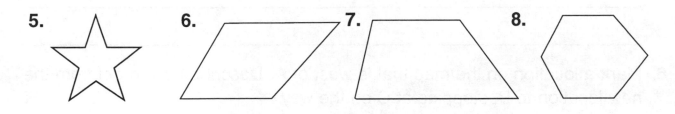

5.   6.   7.   8.

Grade 4
Use after Unit 8.

TEST

Unit 8 (Placing Figures in Space)

Test 2

1. Name a solid whose faces are all quadrilaterals. _____

   How many faces does it have? _____

2. Name a solid whose faces are all triangles. _____

   How many faces does it have? _____

3. Identify the base of each net by marking a B on that face.
   Name the solid that can be made from each net.

_____ _____ _____

4. Draw a line from each name to the correct quadrilateral.

   rhombus

   trapezoid

   parallelogram

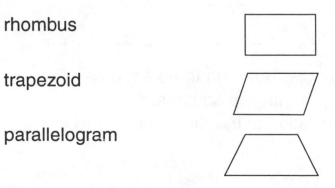

Unit 8 (Placing Figures in Space)

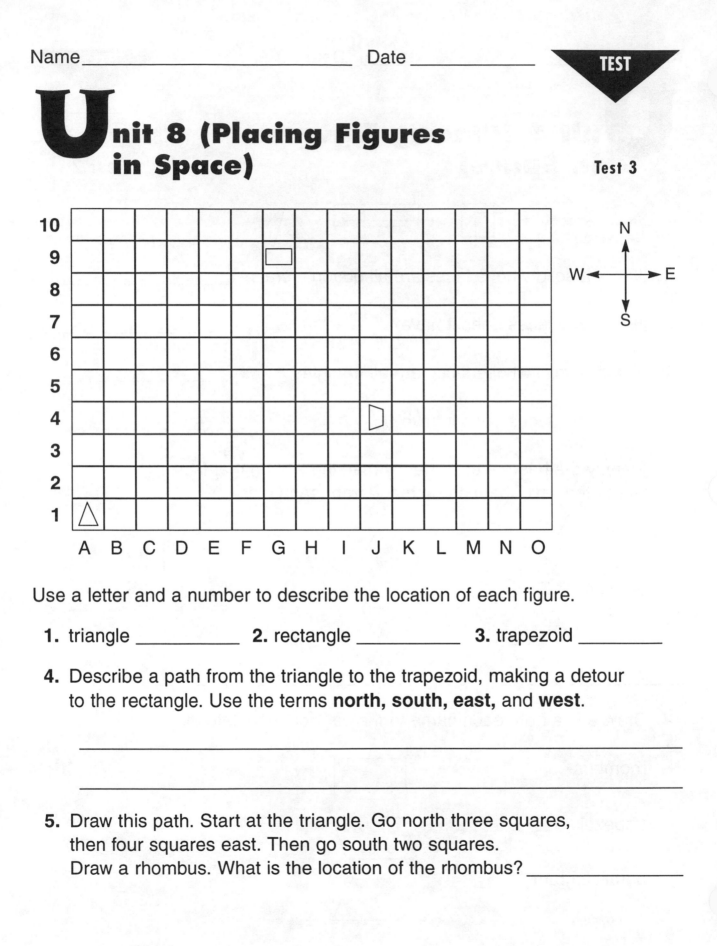

Use a letter and a number to describe the location of each figure.

1. triangle _____   **2.** rectangle _____   **3.** trapezoid _____

4. Describe a path from the triangle to the trapezoid, making a detour
to the rectangle. Use the terms **north**, **south**, **east**, and **west**.

_____

_____

5. Draw this path. Start at the triangle. Go north three squares,
then four squares east. Then go south two squares.
Draw a rhombus. What is the location of the rhombus? _____

© Addison-Wesley Publishers Limited

Identifying Patterns

Complete each pattern. Then describe the pattern.

1. 27, 37, 47, _____, _____, _____, 87

Pattern: _____

2. 15, 30, 45, _____, _____, _____, 105, _____, 135

Pattern: _____

3. 263, 283, 303, _____, _____, 363, _____, _____

Pattern: _____

4. 4790, 4890, 4990, _____, 5190, _____, _____

Pattern: _____

5. 403, 504, 605, _____, _____, _____, _____, 1110

Pattern: _____

6. 901, 811, 721, 631, _____, _____, 361, _____, _____

Pattern: _____

7. 23 456, 24 456, 25 456, _____, _____, _____

Pattern: _____

Name_____ Date _____

Using Patterns

1. Study Juan's sticker design. Suppose Juan puts 3, 4, 5, or 6 creatures in a horizontal row across the middle. Complete the chart below to show the number of stars he will need.

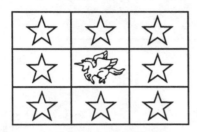   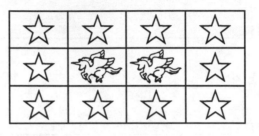

Number of Creatures	1	2	3	4	5	6
Number of Stars	8	10				

2. Juan also designs stickers with a diamond pattern. Study the pattern. Then answer the questions below.

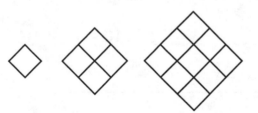

How many diamonds will Juan need for the fourth design?

_____

How many diamonds will Juan need for the fifth design?

_____

Grade 4
Use with Unit 9, Activity 1.

Using T-Tables (1)

Study each pattern. Complete the table.
Then write the rule below the table.
Some rules have been started for you.

1.

First Number	Second Number
1	5
2	10
3	15
4	__
5	__
6	__

Multiply by _____.

2.

First Number	Second Number
4	11
5	12
6	13
7	__
8	__
9	__

Add _____.

3.

First Number	Second Number
21	15
20	14
19	13
18	__
17	__
16	__

_____.

4.

First Number	Second Number
2	14
7	49
4	28
8	__
1	__
9	__

_____.

5.

First Number	Second Number
9	6
3	0
11	8
8	__
4	__
12	__

_____.

6.

First Number	Second Number
8	20
20	32
13	25
4	__
10	__
15	__

_____.

Using T-Tables (2)

1. Study the pattern.
Complete the T-table.
Describe the relationship between the
number of pentagons and the perimeter.

Number of Pentagons	Perimeter of Figure
1	5
2	8
3	____
4	____
5	____

_____

Study the hexagon patterns. Create a T-table to show the relationship
between the number of hexagons and the perimeter of the figure.
Continue the T-table for 2 more figures.

2.

_____

Predict the perimeter of a row of ten hexagons. _____

3.

_____

Predict the perimeter of the sixth figure in the pattern. _____

Grade 4
Use with Unit 9, Activity 2.

▼ **TEST**

Unit 9 (Discovering Patterns and Relationships)

Test 1

Continue each pattern.

1. 7, 9, 11, _____, _____, _____, _____, _____

2. 18, 15, 12, _____, _____, _____, _____

3. 1, 4, 7, 10, _____, _____, _____

4. 25, 21, 17, 13, _____, _____, _____

5. 8, 10, 12, _____, _____, _____, _____

6. 7, 13, 19, 25, _____, _____, _____, _____

7. 23, 33, 43, _____, _____, _____

8. 5, 9, 13, _____, _____, _____

9. 21, 32, 43, 54, _____, _____, _____

10. 735, 725, 715, _____, _____, _____

Unit 9 (Discovering Patterns and Relationships)

Test 2

1. Look for a pattern. Use objects or draw a picture to help you complete the table below.

Number of Squares	1	2	3	4			
Perimeter	4	6	8				

Complete the table for each pattern of alien drawings.

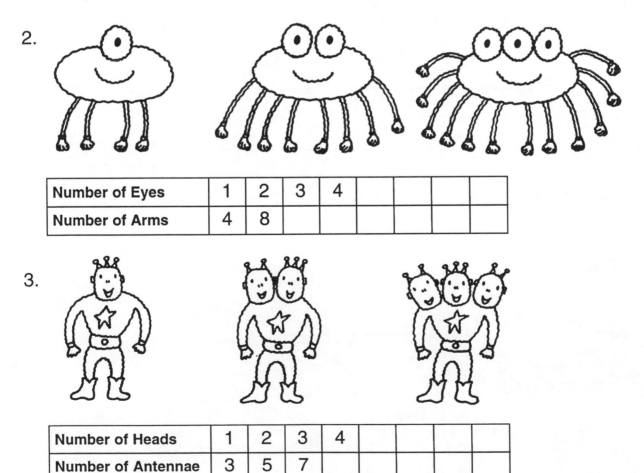

2.

Number of Eyes	1	2	3	4			
Number of Arms	4	8					

3.

Number of Heads	1	2	3	4			
Number of Antennae	3	5	7				

Grade 4
Use after Unit 9.

Name_____ Date _____

Exploring Outcomes

Suppose you are presented with each offer below. Decide whether it would be wise for you to take it. Explain your decisions.

1. Either you or your brother takes out the garbage. Your brother says to you, "I will roll this number cube. If I roll a 3 or higher, you take out the garbage for a month. If I roll less than a 3, I will." Should you take this offer?

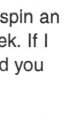

_____

_____

2. Either you or your sister walks the dogs. She says to you, "I will spin this spinner. If I spin an odd number, you walk the dogs this week. If I spin an even number, I will do it." Should you take her offer?

_____

_____

3. Either you or your sister has to clean the yard. She makes you this offer: She will mix up these four number cards and place them face down on a table. Then she will turn over two of them. If the sum is 6 or greater, she will clean the yard. Otherwise, you will. Should you take her offer?

_____

_____

Name_____ Date _____

Predicting Outcomes

Try this experiment.
Cut out four red squares, two blue squares, and one yellow square.
Be sure they are all the same size. Put them into a bag.

1. Suppose someone reaches in and
   takes a square without looking.
   Which colour is most likely to be picked? _____
   Which colour is least likely to be picked? _____
   Explain why you predicted these colours.

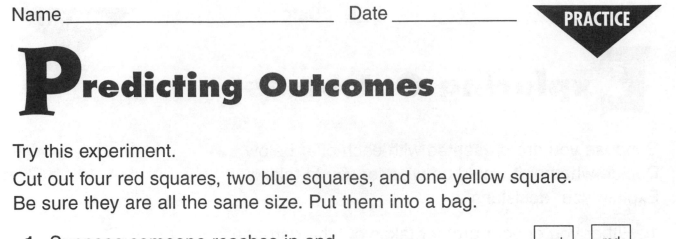

   _____

   _____

   _____

red	blue	yellow

2. Take one square from the bag. Return the square to the bag.
   Do this 30 times. Record each colour drawn with tally marks.

3. Draw a bar graph to show the outcomes.

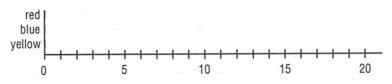

4. How close were the results to your predictions?

   _____

   _____

5. Suppose you try the experiment again. This time, you use equal
   numbers of red, blue, and yellow squares. How would a bar graph
   for this experiment differ from your first one? Explain.

   _____

   _____

Grade 4
Use with Unit 10, Activity 2.

Name_____ Date _____

Finding All Outcomes

Make two spinners like these:

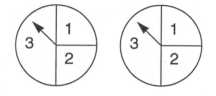

1. Suppose you spin the two spinners 30 times.
   You find the sum of the two numbers each time.
   List all the possible outcomes.   _____

   Predict which sum you would spin the most.   _____

   Predict which sum you would spin the least.   _____

2. Test your predictions. Spin 30 times.
   Record your results in the table.

Sum	Tally

3. How did your results compare
   with your predictions?

   _____

   _____

4. Suppose you made two identical
   spinners with three different numbers.
   When you spun them, the sum that
   came up most often was 8. The sum that
   came up least often was 12. Show one way
   the spinners might look.

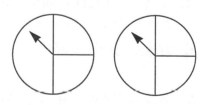

Name_____ Date _____

Finding Combinations

Sandy's Sandwich Stop offers these daily specials.

Breads	Fillings	Extras
white sourdough pita	any meat tuna cheese	lettuce tomato mayonnaise

1. Suppose you chose pita bread. You will have one filling and one extra. List all the possible combinations you could have.

   _____

   _____

   _____

2. Ramon does not like mayonnaise or meat. How many combinations of one filling and one extra with pita are there for him? _____

3. Tessa likes either white or sourdough bread and any filling. If she adds mayonnaise, she never adds it to cheese. How many combinations of bread, one filling, and one extra are there for her? _____

Suppose that a customer orders a sandwich with one filling and one extra. Use one of the terms **possible**, **impossible**, **certain**, or **uncertain** to describe each order.

4. a sandwich using pita bread _____

5. a sandwich with mayonnaise _____

6. a sandwich using white, sourdough, or pita bread _____

7. tuna with tomato on whole wheat bread _____

Grade 4
Use with Unit 10, Activity 4.

Analyzing Outcomes

Think about the objects in each set of playing pieces. Write whether the outcome given is **very likely, not very likely,** or **likely** to occur.

1. Outcome: toss tails and roll a 5

_____

2. Outcome: toss heads and roll any number

_____

3. Outcome: spin black and spin 3

_____

4. Outcome: spin black and pick 66

_____

5. Outcome: spin any colour but black and pick any number but 66

_____

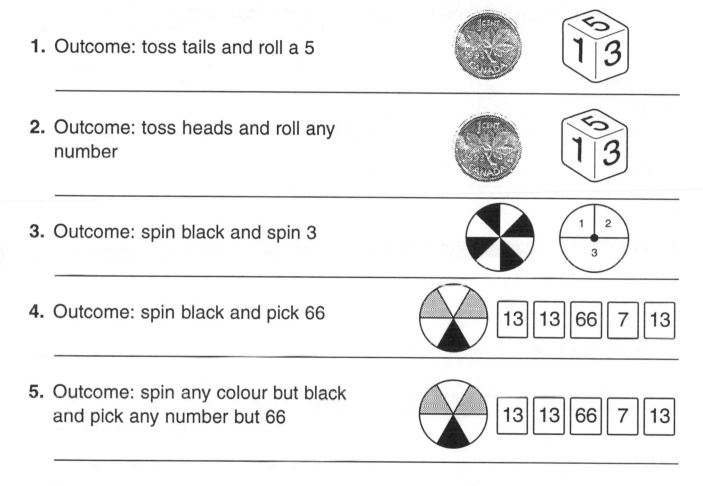

6. Suppose you are making a coloured spinner and a set of six cards. You want it to be very likely to spin red and draw an even number. What colours would you use on the spinner? What numbers would you use on the cards? Write or draw to show what you think.

_____

_____

Unit 10 (Exploring Outcomes)

Test 1

The table shows people who are trying out for the sing-down. Everyone must sing as a pair. Each pair needs a high voice and a low voice.

High Voices	Low Voices
Suzy	Marcia
Yasmina	David
Tim	Ethan
Joyce	Peter

Use the table. Answer the questions.

1. How many different partners could Yasmina have? _____

2. Can Suzy and Joyce form a pair? Explain. _____

_____

3. List all the possible pairs. _____

_____

_____

_____

_____

4. How many boy-girl pairs are possible? _____

5. How likely is it that Yasmina and Marcia will form a pair?_____

_____

6. Suppose Yasmina and Marcia sing together. Then, new pairs are formed. How likely is it that Yasmina and Marcia will sing together a second time?

_____

Unit 10 (Exploring Outcomes)

Test 2

Predict the number of times you must flip a coin to have it land heads five times.

_____

Follow these steps to do an experiment.

- Get a coin.

- Flip it as many times as necessary until it lands heads five times. Record the number of flips.

- Repeat the steps nine more times. Each time, keep a separate record of the number of flips.

Use the results of the experiment. Answer these questions.

1. Explain what happened in the experiment. _____

2. Predict the number of flips necessary to get five heads.

_____

3. How certain are you of your prediction? _____

4. What could you do to make a better prediction?

_____

Unit 10 (Exploring Outcomes)

Test 3

1. Make these cards:

Suppose you placed the cards in a bag, then drew a card and returned it to the bag. You did this 50 times.

Predict the number of odd numbers you will get.

_____

Now try it. Tally your results.

Even	Odd

How did your results compare with your prediction?

_____

2. Make these cards:

Suppose you placed the cards in a bag, then drew a card and returned it to the bag. You did this 30 times.

Predict whether you will get more W's, more L's, or about the same number of W's and L's.

_____

_____

Now try it. Tally your results.

W's	L's

How did your results compare with your prediction?

_____

Measuring in Centimetres (1)

Find the length of each worm to the nearest centimetre.

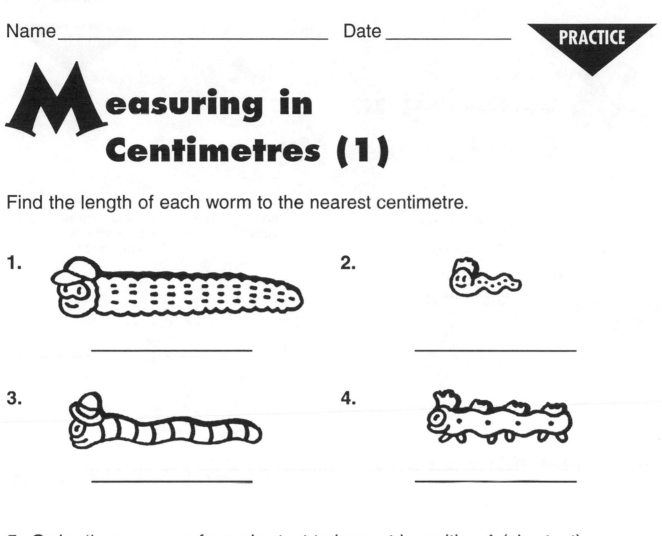

1.

_____

2.

_____

3.

_____

4.

_____

5. Order these worms from shortest to longest by writing **1** (shortest), **2,** and **3** (longest).

_____   _____   _____

Draw a worm of each length.

6. 7 cm

7. 5 cm

8. 2 cm

9. 7.5 cm

Measuring in Centimetres (2)

Estimate whether each line segment is **longer** or **shorter** than 10 cm. Then measure each line segment. Record the number of centimetres you would add or subtract to make it 10 cm.

Is it longer or shorter than 10 cm?	How many centimetres would you add or subtract?
1. _____	_____
2. _____	_____
3. _____	_____
4. _____	_____

1. _____

2. _____

3. _____

4. _____

Write whether each statement is **reasonable** or **unreasonable**.

5. A grade 4 student is 175 cm tall. _____

6. This page is about 28 cm long. _____

7. My smile is about 7 cm wide. _____

8. My pen is about 1.4 cm long. _____

9. A toothpick is about 14.5 cm long. _____

10. A coin is about 2 cm wide. _____

Measuring in Millimetres (1)

Find the length of each object to the nearest millimetre.
Record each length in millimetres and centimetres.

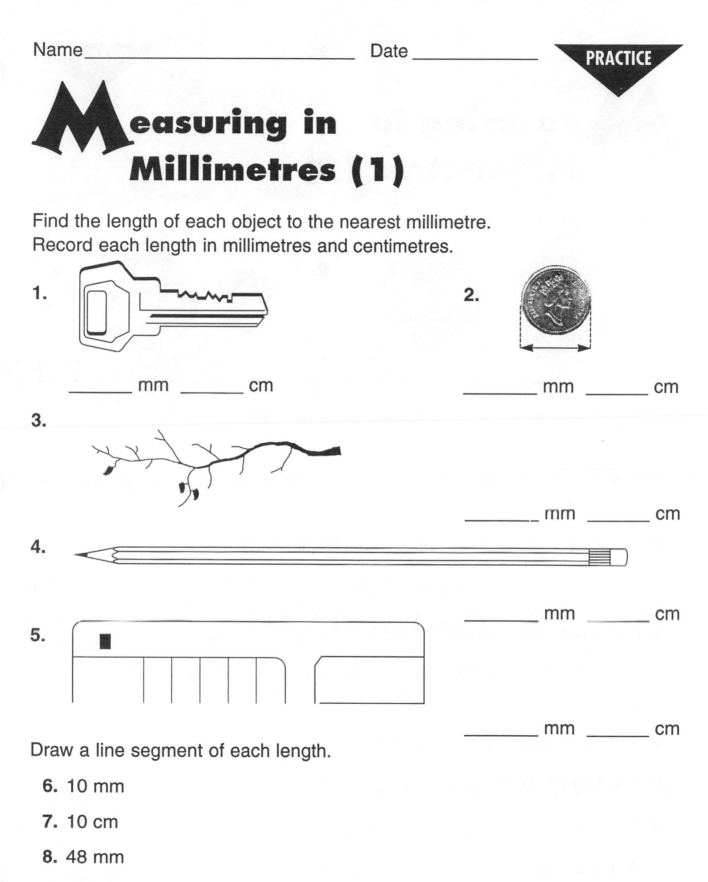

1.

_____ mm _____ cm

2.

_____ mm _____ cm

3.

_____ mm _____ cm

4.

_____ mm _____ cm

5.

_____ mm _____ cm

Draw a line segment of each length.

6. 10 mm

7. 10 cm

8. 48 mm

9. 25 mm

Measuring in Millimetres (2)

Which is wider? How much wider?

1.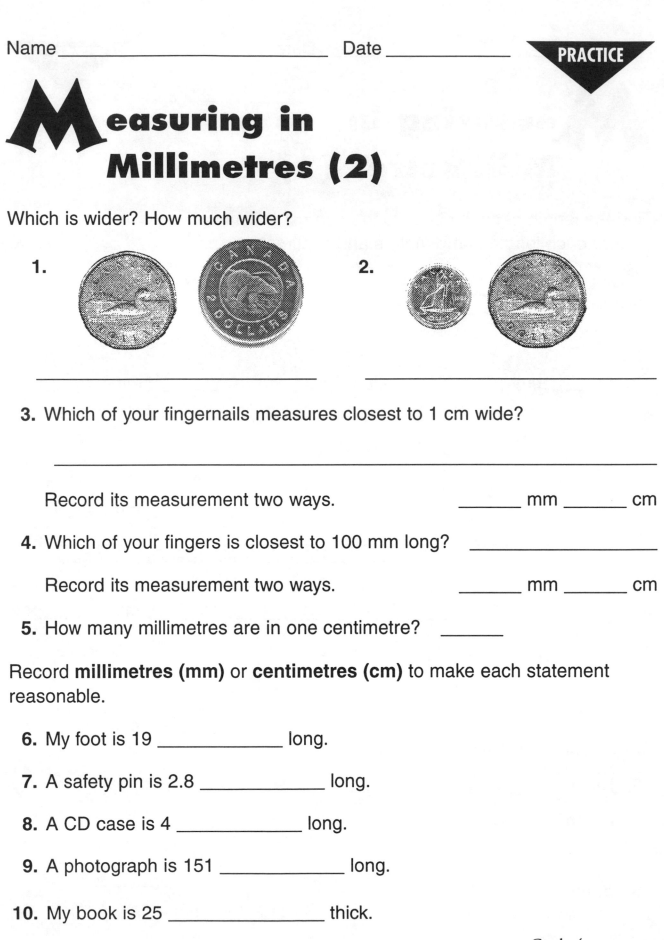

2.

_____

_____

3. Which of your fingernails measures closest to 1 cm wide?

_____

   Record its measurement two ways. _____ mm _____ cm

4. Which of your fingers is closest to 100 mm long? _____

   Record its measurement two ways. _____ mm _____ cm

5. How many millimetres are in one centimetre? _____

Record **millimetres (mm)** or **centimetres (cm)** to make each statement reasonable.

6. My foot is 19 _____ long.

7. A safety pin is 2.8 _____ long.

8. A CD case is 4 _____ long.

9. A photograph is 151 _____ long.

10. My book is 25 _____ thick.

Name_____ Date _____

Measuring in Metres (1)

Dinah is a dinosaur fan. She has made a table of the lengths of some small dinosaurs she has been studying. Complete the missing metric measures.

Kind of Dinosaur	Length in Centimetres	Length in Metres
Archaeopteryx	97	
Coelophysis	75	
Compsognathus		0.91
Fabrosaurus		0.95
Homalocephale	80	
Hypsilophodon		0.90
Pachycephalosaurus		0.99
Scutellosaurus	72	

Use the data. Answer each question.

1. Which dinosaur is the longest? _____

2. Which dinosaur is second longest? _____

3. Which dinosaur is the shortest? _____

4. Which dinosaur is 0.75 m long? _____

5. How much longer would the Archaeopteryx
   have to be to reach 1 m in length? _____

Name_____ Date _____

Measuring in Metres (2)

1. Find three objects that you estimate are longer than 1 m.
Draw a picture of each object in the chart.
Estimate the length of each object in metres.
Then measure the length. Complete the chart.

Object	Estimated Length	Measured Length	Did you *overestimate* or *underestimate?*

2. Find the number of heel-to-toe steps you take to walk 1 m. _____
Predict the number of heel-to-toe steps you would take to walk:

10 m   _____   1 km   _____

100 m   _____   50 cm   _____

3. How many centimetres are in one metre? _____

4. How many metres are in one kilometre? _____

Grade 4
Use with Unit 11, Activity 3.

Measuring Capacity (1)

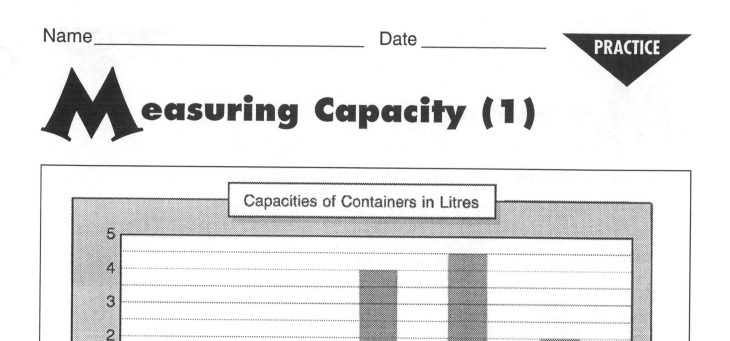

1. What is the capacity of container A? _____

2. Which container has a capacity of 2 L? _____

3. Which containers have capacities greater than 1 L?

_____

4. List the containers in order from least to greatest capacity.

_____

Circle a reasonable estimate of the capacity of each item.

5. bathroom sink: 1 to 2 L   5 to 10 L   15 to 20 L

6. cereal bowl: less than 1 L   1 to 2 L   more than 2 L

7. mixing bowl: less than 1 L   1 to 2 L   more than 5 L

Grade 4
Use with Unit 11, Activity 4.

Measuring Capacity (2)

Circle the measures.

1. Measures of containers in which milk is typically sold.

25 mL   250 mL   250 L   1 L   1 mL   2 L   4 mL   4 L

2. The measure that is closest to one litre.

750 mL   7500 mL   1250 mL   850 mL

Circle a reasonable estimate of the capacity of each item.

3. toothpaste tube: 25 to 75 mL   100 to 200 mL   over 200 mL

4. juice box: 25 to 75 mL   100 to 200 mL   over 200 mL

5. shampoo bottle: 25 to 75 mL   100 to 200 mL   over 200 mL

6. ice cream scoop: 25 to 75 mL   100 to 200 mL   over 200 mL

Record **millilitres (mL)** or **litres (L)** to make each statement reasonable.

7. My cereal spoon holds 10 _____ of milk.

8. My fish tank holds 10 _____ of water.

9. A juice glass holds 150 _____ of juice.

10. A carton of milk holds 1000 _____ of milk.

142

Measuring Mass (1)

Circle a reasonable estimate of the mass of each item.

1. a handful of coins: less than 1 kg   about 1 kg   more than 1 kg

2. a baby: less than 1 kg   about 1 kg   more than 1 kg

3. a chicken: less than 1 kg   about 1 kg   more than 1 kg

4. a volleyball: less than 1 kg   about 1 kg   more than 1 kg

5. your math textbook: less than 1 kg   about 1 kg   more than 1 kg

6. a bag of potatoes: less than 1 kg   about 1 kg   more than 1 kg

7. A deer has a mass of about 180 kg. About how many grade 4 students would equal the mass of a deer?

_____

8. About how many 10-kg infants would equal the mass of a 9-year-old?

_____

9. A banana has a mass of about 200 g. About how many bananas would it take to make 1 kg?

_____

Measuring Mass (2)

Circle the greater mass in each pair.

1. 35 kg   or   3.5 kg   **2.** 35 g   or   3.5 kg

3. 3000 g   or   2 kg   **4.** 5 kg   or   500 g

5. Circle the mass that is closest to two kilograms.

    3000 g   2000 g   2.1 kg   500 g

Circle a reasonable estimate of the mass of each item.

6. a granola bar: less than 10 g   50 to 100 g   over 200 g

7. a loonie coin: less than 10 g   50 to 100 g   over 200 g

8. a full lunch box: less than 10 g   50 to 100 g   over 200 g

9. an orange: less than 10 g   50 to 100 g   over 200 g

Record **grams (g)** or **kilograms (kg)** to make each statement reasonable.

10. My mass is about 30 000 _____.

11. I bought a 2- _____ bag of rice.

12. A table-tennis ball has a mass of about 2 _____.

13. A basketball has a mass of about 0.5 _____.

Grade 4
Use with Unit 11, Activity 5.

Unit 11
(Relating Measures)

Test 1

Choose an interesting object in the classroom or at home. It might be a piece of furniture, a toy, a tool, an instrument, or a piece of sports equipment. Sketch it below. Measure as many dimensions of the object as you can. Clearly label each measurement on your sketch.

Name_____ Date _____

Unit 11
(Relating Measures)   Test 2

Record the best unit for each measure.

millimetres	centimetres	metres	kilometres

1. your height   _____

2. the distance from home to school   _____

3. the thickness of a coin   _____

4. the length of a peanut   _____

5. the length of a drinking straw   _____

6. the length of your classroom   _____

Circle the greater measure in each pair.

7. 5 cm   or   4.5 cm   8. 55 cm   or   55 mm

9. 80 cm   or   80 m   10. 900 m   or   1 km

11. Which would you rather have, 50 cm of quarters placed side by side, or
    0.5 m of quarters placed side by side? Explain.

_____

12. Suppose you can ride your bike one kilometre in about ten minutes.

    About how long would it take you to ride 5 km? _____

    About how long would it take you to ride 500 m? _____

146

Grade 4
Use after Unit 11.

Name_____ Date _____ ▼ TEST

Unit 11
(Relating Measures)   Test 3

Write a unit of measure to make each statement reasonable.

| kg | cm | m | g | mL | mm | L | km |

1. We will travel about 15 _____ a day on our canoe trip.

2. Our tent has a mass of about 4 _____.

3. Each drinking cup holds about 250 _____ each.

4. Each water bottle holds about 1000 _____ each.

5. The canoe is about 6 _____ long.

6. Each backpack is about 100 _____ tall.

7. My sleeping bag is about 180 _____ long.

8. We'll take a 120- _____ bottle of sunscreen.

9. The longest portage we will do is about 850 _____.

10. A sleeping bag has a mass of over 1000 _____.

Grade 4
Use after Unit 11.

147

TEST

Unit 11
(Relating Measures)

Test 4

Circle the greater measure in each pair.

1. 50 mL   or   250 mL

2. 50 mL   or   50 L

3. 100 g   or   100 kg

4. 500 g   or   1 kg

Describe the capacity of each container as **less than one litre**, **about one litre**, or **greater than one litre**.

5. one serving of soup

_____

6. a washing machine tub

_____

7. a kettle

_____

8. a bottle of ketchup

_____

Answer each question.

9. Name three items that are measured in grams.

_____

10. Suppose a small orange has a mass of about 100 g.
How many oranges would be in 1 kg?   _____

11. Which would you rather have: 250 mL of juice or 250 L of juice? Explain.

_____

12. Suppose you have 8 L of juice. Is there enough to give each student in your class one glass? Explain.

_____

148

Grade 4
Use after Unit 11.

Skills Bank

Name _____

My Skills Bank Record Chart

These are pages in the Skills Bank that I have completed.

Page	Check (✔) if complete	Date
152 Writing Numbers		
153 Rounding Numbers		
154 Adding, Sums 1 to 18		
155 Subtracting from 1 to 18		
156 Adding (1)		
157 Adding (2)		
158 Subtracting (1)		
159 Subtracting (2)		
160 Multiplying, Groups of 0, 1, 2, and 5		
161 Multiplying, Groups of 3 and 6		
162 Multiplying, Groups of 4 and 8		
163 Multiplying, Groups of 7 and 9		
164 Multiplying, Groups of 6 to 9		
165 Multiplying, Groups of 0 to 9		
166 Dividing, Divisors 1, 2, and 3		
167 Dividing, Divisors 4, 5, and 6		

Grade 4

My Skills Bank Record Chart

Page	Check (✔) if complete	Date
168 Dividing, Divisors 7, 8, and 9		
169 Dividing, Divisors 1 to 5		
170 Dividing, Divisors 6 to 9		
171 Dividing, Divisors 1 to 9		
172 Multiplying (1)		
173 Muliplying (2)		
174 Multiplying by 10 and 100		
175 Multiplying by Multiples of 10		
176 Dividing, Divisors 2 to 5, Remainders		
177 Dividing, Divisors 6 to 9, Remainders		
178 Dividing, Two-Digit Quotients, No Remainders		
179 Dividing, Two-Digit Quotients, Remainders		
180 Telling Time		
181 Renaming Decimals as Fractions		
182 Renaming Fractions as Decimals		

Writing Numbers

Write the numeral for each.

1. eight hundred forty-five _____

2. one hundred seven _____

3. nine hundred seventy _____

4. eight thousand nine hundred _____

5. nine thousand seventy _____

6. nine thousand seventeen _____

Write each number in words.

7. 678 _____

8. 407 _____

9. 919 _____

10. 5029 _____

11. 8008 _____

12. 3013 _____

Rounding Numbers

Round each number to the nearest ten.

1. 49 _____ **2.** 21 _____ **3.** 54 _____

4. 217 _____ **5.** 384 _____ **6.** 605 _____

Round each number to the nearest hundred.

7. 882 _____ **8.** 739 _____ **9.** 550 _____

10. 3261 _____ **11.** 6470 _____ **12.** 19 109 _____

Round each number to the nearest thousand.

13. 4527 _____ **14.** 7266 _____ **15.** 9715 _____

16. 37 814 _____ **17.** 59 630 _____ **18.** 62 473 _____

SKILLS BANK

Adding, Sums 1 to 18

Find each sum.

1.

6	8	7	8	9	0	9
+2	+3	+2	+5	+3	+7	+1

2.

5	8	6	3	6	8	5
+2	+1	+6	+8	+3	+4	+5

3.

7	2	0	5	8	2	5
+1	+9	+6	+9	+8	+7	+6

4.

4	3	7	8	5	6	7
+7	+4	+6	+7	+3	+9	+7

5.

8	1	3	7	7	9	5
+9	+8	+7	+5	+9	+4	+1

6.

9	5	4	7	8	9	3
+7	+8	+5	+8	+2	+6	+9

7.

6	2	9	9	9	8	9
+4	+1	+8	+5	+0	+6	+9

Grade 4, Skills Bank
Use any time.

Subtracting from 1 to 18

Find each difference.

1.
$$\begin{array}{r} 5 \\ -1 \end{array}\qquad \begin{array}{r} 6 \\ -6 \end{array}\qquad \begin{array}{r} 17 \\ -9 \end{array}\qquad \begin{array}{r} 8 \\ -5 \end{array}\qquad \begin{array}{r} 14 \\ -8 \end{array}\qquad \begin{array}{r} 10 \\ -7 \end{array}\qquad \begin{array}{r} 8 \\ -3 \end{array}$$

2.
$$\begin{array}{r} 4 \\ -0 \end{array}\qquad \begin{array}{r} 9 \\ -3 \end{array}\qquad \begin{array}{r} 18 \\ -9 \end{array}\qquad \begin{array}{r} 12 \\ -8 \end{array}\qquad \begin{array}{r} 13 \\ -6 \end{array}\qquad \begin{array}{r} 8 \\ -4 \end{array}\qquad \begin{array}{r} 5 \\ -5 \end{array}$$

3.
$$\begin{array}{r} 11 \\ -2 \end{array}\qquad \begin{array}{r} 14 \\ -5 \end{array}\qquad \begin{array}{r} 6 \\ -5 \end{array}\qquad \begin{array}{r} 12 \\ -9 \end{array}\qquad \begin{array}{r} 16 \\ -8 \end{array}\qquad \begin{array}{r} 10 \\ -1 \end{array}\qquad \begin{array}{r} 16 \\ -9 \end{array}$$

4.
$$\begin{array}{r} 14 \\ -7 \end{array}\qquad \begin{array}{r} 4 \\ -3 \end{array}\qquad \begin{array}{r} 11 \\ -6 \end{array}\qquad \begin{array}{r} 10 \\ -2 \end{array}\qquad \begin{array}{r} 13 \\ -8 \end{array}\qquad \begin{array}{r} 16 \\ -7 \end{array}\qquad \begin{array}{r} 9 \\ -9 \end{array}$$

5.
$$\begin{array}{r} 15 \\ -9 \end{array}\qquad \begin{array}{r} 17 \\ -8 \end{array}\qquad \begin{array}{r} 10 \\ -6 \end{array}\qquad \begin{array}{r} 7 \\ -5 \end{array}\qquad \begin{array}{r} 12 \\ -7 \end{array}\qquad \begin{array}{r} 9 \\ -4 \end{array}\qquad \begin{array}{r} 11 \\ -5 \end{array}$$

6.
$$\begin{array}{r} 9 \\ -5 \end{array}\qquad \begin{array}{r} 15 \\ -8 \end{array}\qquad \begin{array}{r} 12 \\ -5 \end{array}\qquad \begin{array}{r} 14 \\ -7 \end{array}\qquad \begin{array}{r} 14 \\ -6 \end{array}\qquad \begin{array}{r} 11 \\ -7 \end{array}\qquad \begin{array}{r} 9 \\ -7 \end{array}$$

7.
$$\begin{array}{r} 13 \\ -5 \end{array}\qquad \begin{array}{r} 8 \\ -6 \end{array}\qquad \begin{array}{r} 12 \\ -4 \end{array}\qquad \begin{array}{r} 8 \\ -7 \end{array}\qquad \begin{array}{r} 10 \\ -4 \end{array}\qquad \begin{array}{r} 11 \\ -8 \end{array}\qquad \begin{array}{r} 14 \\ -9 \end{array}$$

Grade 4, Skills Bank
Use any time.

Adding (1)

Find each sum.

1.	32 + 95	**2.**	64 + 27	**3.**	63 + 83	**4.**	91 + 75

5.	86 + 27	**6.**	55 + 64	**7.**	73 + 87	**8.**	49 + 59

9.	127 + 462	**10.**	609 + 234	**11.**	435 + 417	**12.**	588 + 124

13.	380 + 946	**14.**	937 + 509	**15.**	264 + 876	**16.**	716 + 456

17.	822 + 37	**18.**	196 + 53	**19.**	487 + 28	**20.**	634 + 92

21.	56 + 307	**22.**	83 + 488	**23.**	70 + 563	**24.**	95 + 688

25.	$0.37 +$0.69	**26.**	$0.56 + $0.74	**27.**	$1.42 + $1.87	**28.**	$4.07 + $3.37

Grade 4, Skills Bank
Use any time.

 dding (2)

Find each sum.

1. 3247 + 5631	**2.** 5015 + 2804	**3.** 6438 + 1623	**4.** 7627 + 1758
5. 9426 + 1488	**6.** 8374 + 4276	**7.** 4308 + 4993	**8.** 2975 + 6658
9. 3271 + 4389	**10.** 2045 + 9271	**11.** 3563 + 4539	**12.** 5041 + 8665
13. 8489 + 601	**14.** 193 + 3572	**15.** 5057 + 963	**16.** 518 + 4806
17. $28.16 + $25.48	**18.** $39.20 + $42.09	**19.** $53.67 + $48.91	**20.** $16.93 $ 8.17
21. 47 182 19 8 + 231	**22.** 564 607 92 65 + 816	**23.** 8 48 3 140 + 7	**24.** 65 321 8406 934 + 87

Subtracting (1)

Find each difference.

1. 48 − 23	**2.** 63 − 13	**3.** 97 − 84	**4.** 85 − 23
5. 51 − 27	**6.** 74 − 68	**7.** 75 − 29	**8.** 66 − 37
9. 81 − 29	**10.** 90 − 59	**11.** 48 − 19	**12.** 54 − 27
13. 664 − 123	**14.** 752 − 236	**15.** 891 − 608	**16.** 428 − 194
17. 347 − 295	**18.** 924 − 669	**19.** 570 − 298	**20.** 617 − 378
21. 800 − 237	**22.** 702 − 68	**23.** 910 − 65	**24.** 500 − 194

Grade 4, Skills Bank
Use any time.

Subtracting (2)

Find each difference.

1. 6148
    − 1026

2. 7355
    − 2143

3. 8561
    − 2438

4. 9627
    − 6175

5. 7624
    − 5089

6. 6913
    − 3897

7. 9045
    − 6219

8. 3186
    − 2868

9. 5518
    − 2879

10. 4037
    − 1368

11. 3800
    − 3745

12. 8005
    − 3767

13. $36.42
    − $29.61

14. $50.50
    − $45.75

15. $73.06
    − $59.73

16. $91.18
    − $66.07

17. 6014
    − 385

18. 4285
    − 926

19. 7842
    − 238

20. 5346
    − 908

21. 9203
    − 650

22. 3651
    − 260

23. 6458
    − 793

24. 5217
    − 769

Grade 4, Skills Bank
Use any time.

Multiplying, Groups of 0, 1, 2, and 5

Find each product.

1.	1 ×9	2 ×6	2 ×1	1 ×0	2 ×4	2 ×3	1 ×4
2.	1 ×2	5 ×4	2 ×9	1 ×3	2 ×3	2 ×8	1 ×5
3.	2 ×7	1 ×1	5 ×7	5 ×3	0 ×2	2 ×0	1 ×7
4.	1 ×8	5 ×5	2 ×4	2 ×3	5 ×9	1 ×6	0 ×4
5.	5 ×3	5 ×8	2 ×2	2 ×5	2 ×9	5 ×6	5 ×4
6.	0 ×3	5 ×4	5 ×5	2 ×6	1 ×4	2 ×8	5 ×3
7.	5 ×1	2 ×6	5 ×2	5 ×4	0 ×3	5 ×3	5 ×7

Grade 4, Skills Bank
Use any time.

Multiplying, Groups of 3 and 6

Find each product.

1.
$$\begin{array}{r} 6 \\ \times 3 \\ \hline \end{array}$$
$$\begin{array}{r} 3 \\ \times 5 \\ \hline \end{array}$$
$$\begin{array}{r} 3 \\ \times 2 \\ \hline \end{array}$$
$$\begin{array}{r} 3 \\ \times 8 \\ \hline \end{array}$$
$$\begin{array}{r} 3 \\ \times 4 \\ \hline \end{array}$$
$$\begin{array}{r} 3 \\ \times 7 \\ \hline \end{array}$$
$$\begin{array}{r} 3 \\ \times 9 \\ \hline \end{array}$$

2.
$$\begin{array}{r} 3 \\ \times 2 \\ \hline \end{array}$$
$$\begin{array}{r} 3 \\ \times 5 \\ \hline \end{array}$$
$$\begin{array}{r} 3 \\ \times 6 \\ \hline \end{array}$$
$$\begin{array}{r} 3 \\ \times 7 \\ \hline \end{array}$$
$$\begin{array}{r} 3 \\ \times 3 \\ \hline \end{array}$$
$$\begin{array}{r} 3 \\ \times 8 \\ \hline \end{array}$$
$$\begin{array}{r} 3 \\ \times 4 \\ \hline \end{array}$$

3.
$$\begin{array}{r} 3 \\ \times 9 \\ \hline \end{array}$$
$$\begin{array}{r} 3 \\ \times 6 \\ \hline \end{array}$$
$$\begin{array}{r} 3 \\ \times 9 \\ \hline \end{array}$$
$$\begin{array}{r} 3 \\ \times 7 \\ \hline \end{array}$$
$$\begin{array}{r} 3 \\ \times 4 \\ \hline \end{array}$$
$$\begin{array}{r} 3 \\ \times 7 \\ \hline \end{array}$$
$$\begin{array}{r} 3 \\ \times 8 \\ \hline \end{array}$$

4.
$$\begin{array}{r} 6 \\ \times 2 \\ \hline \end{array}$$
$$\begin{array}{r} 6 \\ \times 6 \\ \hline \end{array}$$
$$\begin{array}{r} 6 \\ \times 3 \\ \hline \end{array}$$
$$\begin{array}{r} 6 \\ \times 8 \\ \hline \end{array}$$
$$\begin{array}{r} 6 \\ \times 4 \\ \hline \end{array}$$
$$\begin{array}{r} 6 \\ \times 5 \\ \hline \end{array}$$
$$\begin{array}{r} 6 \\ \times 7 \\ \hline \end{array}$$

5.
$$\begin{array}{r} 6 \\ \times 9 \\ \hline \end{array}$$
$$\begin{array}{r} 6 \\ \times 2 \\ \hline \end{array}$$
$$\begin{array}{r} 6 \\ \times 7 \\ \hline \end{array}$$
$$\begin{array}{r} 6 \\ \times 6 \\ \hline \end{array}$$
$$\begin{array}{r} 6 \\ \times 4 \\ \hline \end{array}$$
$$\begin{array}{r} 6 \\ \times 8 \\ \hline \end{array}$$
$$\begin{array}{r} 6 \\ \times 3 \\ \hline \end{array}$$

6.
$$\begin{array}{r} 6 \\ \times 3 \\ \hline \end{array}$$
$$\begin{array}{r} 6 \\ \times 8 \\ \hline \end{array}$$
$$\begin{array}{r} 6 \\ \times 7 \\ \hline \end{array}$$
$$\begin{array}{r} 6 \\ \times 9 \\ \hline \end{array}$$
$$\begin{array}{r} 6 \\ \times 5 \\ \hline \end{array}$$
$$\begin{array}{r} 6 \\ \times 6 \\ \hline \end{array}$$
$$\begin{array}{r} 6 \\ \times 4 \\ \hline \end{array}$$

7.
$$\begin{array}{r} 6 \\ \times 7 \\ \hline \end{array}$$
$$\begin{array}{r} 3 \\ \times 5 \\ \hline \end{array}$$
$$\begin{array}{r} 3 \\ \times 6 \\ \hline \end{array}$$
$$\begin{array}{r} 6 \\ \times 7 \\ \hline \end{array}$$
$$\begin{array}{r} 6 \\ \times 4 \\ \hline \end{array}$$
$$\begin{array}{r} 6 \\ \times 9 \\ \hline \end{array}$$
$$\begin{array}{r} 3 \\ \times 7 \\ \hline \end{array}$$

Multiplying, Groups of 4 and 8

Find each product.

1.
$$\begin{array}{r} 4 \\ \times 3 \\ \hline \end{array}$$
$$\begin{array}{r} 4 \\ \times 8 \\ \hline \end{array}$$
$$\begin{array}{r} 4 \\ \times 6 \\ \hline \end{array}$$
$$\begin{array}{r} 4 \\ \times 5 \\ \hline \end{array}$$
$$\begin{array}{r} 4 \\ \times 7 \\ \hline \end{array}$$
$$\begin{array}{r} 4 \\ \times 4 \\ \hline \end{array}$$
$$\begin{array}{r} 4 \\ \times 9 \\ \hline \end{array}$$

2.
$$\begin{array}{r} 4 \\ \times 1 \\ \hline \end{array}$$
$$\begin{array}{r} 4 \\ \times 8 \\ \hline \end{array}$$
$$\begin{array}{r} 4 \\ \times 7 \\ \hline \end{array}$$
$$\begin{array}{r} 4 \\ \times 2 \\ \hline \end{array}$$
$$\begin{array}{r} 4 \\ \times 9 \\ \hline \end{array}$$
$$\begin{array}{r} 4 \\ \times 6 \\ \hline \end{array}$$
$$\begin{array}{r} 4 \\ \times 4 \\ \hline \end{array}$$

3.
$$\begin{array}{r} 4 \\ \times 3 \\ \hline \end{array}$$
$$\begin{array}{r} 4 \\ \times 0 \\ \hline \end{array}$$
$$\begin{array}{r} 4 \\ \times 4 \\ \hline \end{array}$$
$$\begin{array}{r} 4 \\ \times 9 \\ \hline \end{array}$$
$$\begin{array}{r} 4 \\ \times 5 \\ \hline \end{array}$$
$$\begin{array}{r} 4 \\ \times 6 \\ \hline \end{array}$$
$$\begin{array}{r} 4 \\ \times 7 \\ \hline \end{array}$$

4.
$$\begin{array}{r} 8 \\ \times 3 \\ \hline \end{array}$$
$$\begin{array}{r} 8 \\ \times 8 \\ \hline \end{array}$$
$$\begin{array}{r} 8 \\ \times 6 \\ \hline \end{array}$$
$$\begin{array}{r} 8 \\ \times 5 \\ \hline \end{array}$$
$$\begin{array}{r} 8 \\ \times 7 \\ \hline \end{array}$$
$$\begin{array}{r} 8 \\ \times 4 \\ \hline \end{array}$$
$$\begin{array}{r} 8 \\ \times 9 \\ \hline \end{array}$$

5.
$$\begin{array}{r} 8 \\ \times 1 \\ \hline \end{array}$$
$$\begin{array}{r} 8 \\ \times 8 \\ \hline \end{array}$$
$$\begin{array}{r} 8 \\ \times 7 \\ \hline \end{array}$$
$$\begin{array}{r} 8 \\ \times 2 \\ \hline \end{array}$$
$$\begin{array}{r} 8 \\ \times 9 \\ \hline \end{array}$$
$$\begin{array}{r} 8 \\ \times 6 \\ \hline \end{array}$$
$$\begin{array}{r} 8 \\ \times 4 \\ \hline \end{array}$$

6.
$$\begin{array}{r} 8 \\ \times 3 \\ \hline \end{array}$$
$$\begin{array}{r} 8 \\ \times 4 \\ \hline \end{array}$$
$$\begin{array}{r} 8 \\ \times 0 \\ \hline \end{array}$$
$$\begin{array}{r} 8 \\ \times 9 \\ \hline \end{array}$$
$$\begin{array}{r} 8 \\ \times 7 \\ \hline \end{array}$$
$$\begin{array}{r} 8 \\ \times 5 \\ \hline \end{array}$$
$$\begin{array}{r} 8 \\ \times 6 \\ \hline \end{array}$$

7.
$$\begin{array}{r} 8 \\ \times 4 \\ \hline \end{array}$$
$$\begin{array}{r} 8 \\ \times 2 \\ \hline \end{array}$$
$$\begin{array}{r} 4 \\ \times 6 \\ \hline \end{array}$$
$$\begin{array}{r} 4 \\ \times 7 \\ \hline \end{array}$$
$$\begin{array}{r} 8 \\ \times 9 \\ \hline \end{array}$$
$$\begin{array}{r} 4 \\ \times 3 \\ \hline \end{array}$$
$$\begin{array}{r} 8 \\ \times 7 \\ \hline \end{array}$$

Grade 4, Skills Bank
Use any time.

Multiplying, Groups of 7 and 9

Find each product.

1.

7	7	7	7	7	7	7
×3	×8	×6	×5	×7	×4	×9

2.

7	7	7	7	7	7	7
×1	×8	×7	×2	×9	×6	×4

3.

7	7	7	7	7	7	7
×3	×0	×4	×9	×5	×6	×7

4.

9	9	9	9	9	9	9
×3	×8	×6	×5	×7	×4	×9

5.

9	9	9	9	9	9	9
×1	×8	×7	×2	×9	×6	×4

6.

9	9	9	9	9	9	9
×3	×4	×0	×8	×7	×5	×6

7.

9	9	7	7	9	7	9
×4	×2	×6	×7	×9	×3	×7

Grade 4, Skills Bank
Use any time.

SKILLS BANK

Multiplying, Groups of 6 to 9

Find each product.

1.	8 ×5	9 ×5	7 ×6	8 ×4	6 ×5	9 ×4	6 ×7

2.	7 ×5	9 ×5	9 ×4	8 ×5	8 ×4	6 ×5	9 ×3

3.	7 ×5	7 ×4	6 ×6	6 ×7	9 ×3	7 ×5	7 ×4

4.	8 ×8	9 ×5	7 ×7	8 ×7	7 ×9	9 ×2	7 ×8

5.	9 ×5	7 ×4	9 ×6	7 ×9	8 ×6	8 ×8	7 ×4

6.	6 ×9	9 ×7	6 ×8	7 ×9	9 ×8	9 ×9	9 ×4

7.	9 ×3	8 ×9	7 ×8	6 ×4	9 ×4	7 ×2	7 ×7

Grade 4, Skills Bank
Use any time.

SKILLS BANK

Multiplying, Groups of 0 to 9

Find each product.

1.
  8   9   7   8   6   9   0
×5   ×5   ×6   ×4   ×5   ×4   ×7

2.
  7   3   9   8   8   6   9
×5   ×5   ×4   ×5   ×4   ×5   ×3

3.
  2   7   6   6   9   7   5
×5   ×4   ×6   ×7   ×3   ×5   ×4

4.
  8   9   3   8   7   9   7
×8   ×5   ×7   ×7   ×9   ×2   ×8

5.
  9   7   9   7   8   4   7
×5   ×4   ×6   ×9   ×6   ×8   ×4

6.
  6   9   6   7   9   9   5
×9   ×7   ×8   ×9   ×8   ×9   ×6

7.
  9   8   1   6   9   7   7
×3   ×9   ×8   ×4   ×4   ×2   ×7

Dividing, Divisors 1, 2, and 3

Find each quotient.

1. $1\overline{)9}$ $1\overline{)7}$ $1\overline{)1}$ $1\overline{)6}$ $1\overline{)2}$

2. $1\overline{)3}$ $1\overline{)8}$ $1\overline{)4}$ $1\overline{)5}$ $1\overline{)0}$

3. $2\overline{)6}$ $2\overline{)14}$ $2\overline{)2}$ $2\overline{)18}$ $2\overline{)8}$

4. $2\overline{)10}$ $2\overline{)0}$ $2\overline{)12}$ $2\overline{)4}$ $2\overline{)16}$

5. $3\overline{)9}$ $3\overline{)3}$ $3\overline{)15}$ $3\overline{)21}$ $3\overline{)12}$

6. $3\overline{)18}$ $3\overline{)27}$ $3\overline{)6}$ $3\overline{)0}$ $3\overline{)24}$

7. $1\overline{)9}$ $3\overline{)15}$ $2\overline{)18}$ $3\overline{)24}$ $3\overline{)12}$

8. $2\overline{)16}$ $3\overline{)27}$ $1\overline{)8}$ $2\overline{)12}$ $3\overline{)18}$

9. $3\overline{)21}$ $1\overline{)1}$ $2\overline{)14}$ $2\overline{)0}$ $2\overline{)10}$

Grade 4, Skills Bank
Use any time.

Dividing, Divisors 4, 5, and 6

Find each quotient.

1. $4\overline{)20}$ $4\overline{)4}$ $4\overline{)32}$ $4\overline{)12}$ $4\overline{)0}$

2. $4\overline{)8}$ $4\overline{)28}$ $4\overline{)36}$ $4\overline{)24}$ $4\overline{)16}$

3. $5\overline{)5}$ $5\overline{)30}$ $5\overline{)10}$ $5\overline{)40}$ $5\overline{)20}$

4. $5\overline{)25}$ $5\overline{)0}$ $5\overline{)15}$ $5\overline{)35}$ $5\overline{)45}$

5. $6\overline{)0}$ $6\overline{)42}$ $6\overline{)6}$ $6\overline{)36}$ $6\overline{)24}$

6. $6\overline{)48}$ $6\overline{)12}$ $6\overline{)30}$ $6\overline{)54}$ $6\overline{)18}$

7. $4\overline{)36}$ $6\overline{)18}$ $5\overline{)45}$ $4\overline{)24}$ $6\overline{)42}$

8. $6\overline{)30}$ $5\overline{)25}$ $6\overline{)24}$ $6\overline{)54}$ $5\overline{)35}$

9. $6\overline{)48}$ $5\overline{)40}$ $5\overline{)30}$ $6\overline{)36}$ $4\overline{)32}$

Dividing, Divisors 7, 8, and 9

Find each quotient.

1. $7\overline{)7}$ $7\overline{)28}$ $7\overline{)14}$ $7\overline{)56}$ $7\overline{)42}$

2. $7\overline{)35}$ $7\overline{)0}$ $7\overline{)49}$ $7\overline{)21}$ $7\overline{)63}$

3. $8\overline{)24}$ $8\overline{)8}$ $8\overline{)48}$ $8\overline{)64}$ $8\overline{)32}$

4. $8\overline{)56}$ $8\overline{)0}$ $8\overline{)72}$ $8\overline{)16}$ $8\overline{)40}$

5. $9\overline{)18}$ $9\overline{)54}$ $9\overline{)0}$ $9\overline{)63}$ $9\overline{)9}$

6. $9\overline{)81}$ $9\overline{)27}$ $9\overline{)36}$ $9\overline{)45}$ $9\overline{)72}$

7. $7\overline{)49}$ $8\overline{)72}$ $9\overline{)63}$ $7\overline{)63}$ $8\overline{)48}$

8. $8\overline{)64}$ $9\overline{)81}$ $7\overline{)42}$ $9\overline{)36}$ $9\overline{)72}$

9. $9\overline{)45}$ $8\overline{)40}$ $9\overline{)54}$ $8\overline{)56}$ $7\overline{)56}$

Grade 4, Skills Bank
Use any time.

Dividing, Divisors 1 to 5

Find each quotient.

1. $5\overline{)15}$ $1\overline{)5}$ $4\overline{)32}$ $3\overline{)0}$ $2\overline{)10}$

2. $4\overline{)4}$ $5\overline{)20}$ $2\overline{)14}$ $4\overline{)36}$ $2\overline{)0}$

3. $1\overline{)0}$ $2\overline{)18}$ $4\overline{)28}$ $3\overline{)9}$ $1\overline{)6}$

4. $5\overline{)40}$ $1\overline{)8}$ $2\overline{)12}$ $4\overline{)0}$ $3\overline{)24}$

5. $1\overline{)9}$ $5\overline{)10}$ $2\overline{)16}$ $3\overline{)21}$ $2\overline{)8}$

6. $1\overline{)3}$ $5\overline{)45}$ $3\overline{)3}$ $4\overline{)16}$ $3\overline{)15}$

7. $1\overline{)4}$ $3\overline{)18}$ $5\overline{)0}$ $2\overline{)2}$ $4\overline{)12}$

8. $5\overline{)35}$ $5\overline{)5}$ $5\overline{)30}$ $3\overline{)12}$ $2\overline{)6}$

9. $4\overline{)24}$ $4\overline{)8}$ $4\overline{)20}$ $3\overline{)27}$ $5\overline{)25}$

Dividing, Divisors 6 to 9

Find each quotient.

1.	6)36	7)7	8)24	6)48	9)27
2.	6)54	7)49	9)72	6)24	7)35
3.	8)56	9)81	8)8	7)21	6)42
4.	7)14	6)30	8)48	7)28	9)18
5.	9)45	7)42	6)54	8)16	7)56
6.	7)63	9)63	8)32	6)6	8)64
7.	9)9	6)12	8)72	9)54	7)49
8.	7)35	6)48	7)14	9)81	8)40
9.	7)63	8)40	9)54	8)56	9)36

Grade 4, Skills Bank
Use any time.

Dividing, Divisors 1 to 9

Find each quotient.

1. $6\overline{)24}$ $7\overline{)21}$ $4\overline{)36}$ $8\overline{)48}$ $9\overline{)45}$

2. $9\overline{)9}$ $8\overline{)64}$ $5\overline{)25}$ $9\overline{)63}$ $3\overline{)15}$

3. $3\overline{)27}$ $6\overline{)36}$ $7\overline{)56}$ $6\overline{)54}$ $5\overline{)40}$

4. $7\overline{)42}$ $6\overline{)30}$ $5\overline{)35}$ $9\overline{)72}$ $4\overline{)20}$

5. $8\overline{)72}$ $4\overline{)28}$ $3\overline{)24}$ $9\overline{)54}$ $6\overline{)18}$

6. $7\overline{)63}$ $9\overline{)81}$ $9\overline{)36}$ $2\overline{)14}$ $8\overline{)40}$

7. $9\overline{)18}$ $6\overline{)48}$ $5\overline{)20}$ $3\overline{)18}$ $7\overline{)49}$

8. $5\overline{)45}$ $6\overline{)42}$ $7\overline{)35}$ $3\overline{)24}$ $2\overline{)18}$

9. $7\overline{)28}$ $8\overline{)56}$ $8\overline{)32}$ $2\overline{)12}$ $5\overline{)30}$

Name_____ Date _____

SKILLS BANK

Multiplying (1)

Find each product.

1. $\begin{array}{r} 19 \\ \times 6 \\ \hline \end{array}$

2. $\begin{array}{r} 92 \\ \times 5 \\ \hline \end{array}$

3. $\begin{array}{r} 28 \\ \times 4 \\ \hline \end{array}$

4. $\begin{array}{r} 83 \\ \times 7 \\ \hline \end{array}$

5. $\begin{array}{r} 48 \\ \times 2 \\ \hline \end{array}$

6. $\begin{array}{r} 75 \\ \times 3 \\ \hline \end{array}$

7. $\begin{array}{r} 65 \\ \times 9 \\ \hline \end{array}$

8. $\begin{array}{r} 36 \\ \times 8 \\ \hline \end{array}$

9. $\begin{array}{r} 57 \\ \times 5 \\ \hline \end{array}$

10. $\begin{array}{r} 18 \\ \times 6 \\ \hline \end{array}$

11. $\begin{array}{r} 86 \\ \times 9 \\ \hline \end{array}$

12. $\begin{array}{r} 94 \\ \times 4 \\ \hline \end{array}$

13. $\begin{array}{r} 25 \\ \times 7 \\ \hline \end{array}$

14. $\begin{array}{r} 43 \\ \times 8 \\ \hline \end{array}$

15. $\begin{array}{r} 69 \\ \times 3 \\ \hline \end{array}$

16. $\begin{array}{r} 72 \\ \times 2 \\ \hline \end{array}$

17. $\begin{array}{r} 39 \\ \times 7 \\ \hline \end{array}$

18. $\begin{array}{r} 76 \\ \times 5 \\ \hline \end{array}$

19. $\begin{array}{r} 85 \\ \times 6 \\ \hline \end{array}$

20. $\begin{array}{r} 64 \\ \times 8 \\ \hline \end{array}$

21. $\begin{array}{r} 77 \\ \times 9 \\ \hline \end{array}$

22. $\begin{array}{r} 93 \\ \times 8 \\ \hline \end{array}$

23. $\begin{array}{r} 68 \\ \times 4 \\ \hline \end{array}$

24. $\begin{array}{r} 89 \\ \times 8 \\ \hline \end{array}$

Grade 4, Skills Bank
Use any time.

 ultiplying (2)

Find each product.

1. 621
   × 2

2. 835
   × 4

3. 716
   × 5

4. 594
   × 6

5. 287
   × 9

6. 903
   × 3

7. 358
   × 7

8. 409
   × 8

9. 590
   × 5

10. 785
   × 3

11. 830
   × 8

12. 667
   × 4

13. 424
   × 9

14. 362
   × 7

15. 953
   × 2

16. 219
   × 6

17. 398
   × 8

18. 567
   × 7

19. 981
   × 9

20. 436
   × 4

21. 705
   × 6

22. 250
   × 5

23. 689
   × 3

24. 840
   × 7

Multiplying by 10 and 100

Find each product.

1.
   10
×6

   10
×5

   10
×2

   10
×7

   10
×9

   10
×3

2.
   10
×57

   10
×28

   10
×40

   10
×98

   10
×77

   10
×35

3.
  122
×10

  455
×10

  268
×10

  729
×10

  402
×10

  833
×10

4.
  100
×3

  100
×7

  100
×5

  100
×9

  100
×2

  100
×1

5.
  100
×45

  100
×66

  100
×27

  100
×98

  100
×31

  100
×16

6.
  100
×74

  100
×12

  100
×23

  100
×59

  100
×21

  100
×34

Grade 4, Skills Bank
Use any time.

Multiplying by Multiples of Ten

Find each product.

1.
20	40	90	70	50
×3	×4	×7	×2	×5

2.
60	80	30	10	40
×9	×3	×6	×9	×8

3.
20	40	30	50	60
×14	×22	×81	×72	×33

4.
10	90	40	20	30
×53	×91	×42	×38	×18

5.
421	535	123	214	322
×10	×10	×60	×20	×30

Grade 4, Skills Bank
Use any time.

Dividing, Divisors
2 to 5, Remainders

Find each quotient.

1. $2\overline{)7}$ 2. $4\overline{)9}$ 3. $3\overline{)10}$ 4. $5\overline{)12}$

5. $5\overline{)21}$ 6. $3\overline{)20}$ 7. $2\overline{)15}$ 8. $4\overline{)14}$

9. $3\overline{)14}$ 10. $2\overline{)9}$ 11. $4\overline{)19}$ 12. $5\overline{)19}$

13. $5\overline{)28}$ 14. $3\overline{)26}$ 15. $2\overline{)11}$ 16. $4\overline{)25}$

17. $4\overline{)30}$ 18. $3\overline{)17}$ 19. $5\overline{)34}$ 20. $2\overline{)17}$

21. $2\overline{)13}$ 22. $4\overline{)39}$ 23. $3\overline{)25}$ 24. $5\overline{)42}$

Grade 4, Skills Bank
Use any time.

Dividing, Divisors 6 to 9, Remainders

Find each quotient.

1. $6\overline{)32}$ 2. $8\overline{)17}$ 3. $7\overline{)24}$ 4. $9\overline{)14}$

5. $7\overline{)46}$ 6. $6\overline{)45}$ 7. $8\overline{)34}$ 8. $9\overline{)32}$

9. $8\overline{)59}$ 10. $9\overline{)62}$ 11. $7\overline{)39}$ 12. $6\overline{)25}$

13. $9\overline{)55}$ 14. $6\overline{)56}$ 15. $8\overline{)76}$ 16. $7\overline{)69}$

17. $6\overline{)40}$ 18. $9\overline{)43}$ 19. $7\overline{)17}$ 20. $8\overline{)45}$

21. $9\overline{)25}$ 22. $7\overline{)58}$ 23. $6\overline{)35}$ 24. $8\overline{)38}$

Dividing, Two-Digit Quotients, No Remainders

Find each quotient.

1.	$2\overline{)48}$	**2.**	$3\overline{)66}$	**3.**	$4\overline{)84}$	**4.**	$5\overline{)50}$
5.	$2\overline{)28}$	**6.**	$3\overline{)90}$	**7.**	$4\overline{)44}$	**8.**	$5\overline{)55}$
9.	$2\overline{)32}$	**10.**	$3\overline{)45}$	**11.**	$4\overline{)64}$	**12.**	$6\overline{)78}$
13.	$3\overline{)87}$	**14.**	$7\overline{)91}$	**15.**	$2\overline{)92}$	**16.**	$4\overline{)72}$
17.	$8\overline{)96}$	**18.**	$6\overline{)84}$	**19.**	$7\overline{)84}$	**20.**	$6\overline{)72}$
21.	$2\overline{)74}$	**22.**	$7\overline{)98}$	**23.**	$6\overline{)90}$	**24.**	$3\overline{)78}$

Grade 4, Skills Bank
Use any time.

Dividing, Two-Digit Quotients, Remainders

Find each quotient.

1. $2\overline{)45}$ 2. $3\overline{)67}$ 3. $4\overline{)70}$ 4. $5\overline{)73}$

5. $2\overline{)51}$ 6. $3\overline{)55}$ 7. $5\overline{)62}$ 8. $4\overline{)91}$

9. $6\overline{)80}$ 10. $4\overline{)83}$ 11. $3\overline{)82}$ 12. $7\overline{)86}$

13. $7\overline{)94}$ 14. $6\overline{)79}$ 15. $4\overline{)66}$ 16. $8\overline{)99}$

17. $4\overline{)51}$ 18. $3\overline{)91}$ 19. $6\overline{)95}$ 20. $7\overline{)74}$

21. $6\overline{)68}$ 22. $8\overline{)90}$ 23. $4\overline{)45}$ 24. $9\overline{)93}$

Telling Time

Write the time shown on each clock.

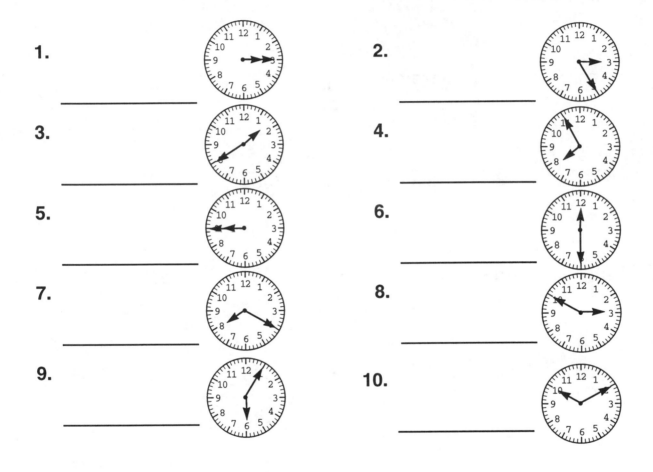

1. _____

_____

2. _____

3. _____

_____

4. _____

_____

5. _____

_____

6. _____

_____

7. _____

_____

8. _____

_____

9. _____

_____

10. _____

_____

Record the time for each activity using **a.m.** or **p.m.**

10. eat breakfast_____   **11.** bed time _____

12. leave for school_____   **13.** lunch time _____

Grade 4 Skills Bank
Use any time

Renaming Decimals as Fractions

Name a fraction for each decimal.
Write more than one fraction for a decimal when you can.

1. 0.1 _____   **2.** 0.5 _____   **3.** 0.7 _____   **4.** 0.9 _____

5. 0.25 _____   **6.** 0.36 _____   **7.** 0.71 _____   **8.** 0.62 _____

9. 0.50 _____   **10.** 0.60 _____   **11.** 0.30 _____   **12.** 0.40 _____

13. 0.04 _____   **14.** 0.07 _____   **15.** 0.01 _____   **16.** 0.02 _____

17. 0.75 _____   **18.** 0.33 _____   **19.** 0.6 _____   **20.** 0.13 _____

21. 0.22 _____   **22.** 0.2 _____   **23.** 0.80 _____   **24.** 0.47 _____

25. 0.66 _____   **26.** 0.59 _____   **27.** 0.85 _____   **28.** 0.8 _____

SKILLS BANK

Renaming Fractions as Decimals

Name a decimal for each fraction.

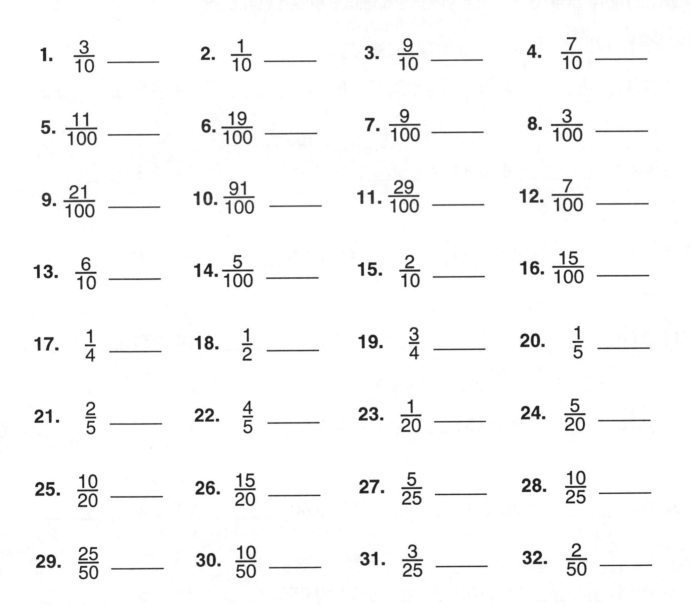

1. $\dfrac{3}{10}$ _____

2. $\dfrac{1}{10}$ _____

3. $\dfrac{9}{10}$ _____

4. $\dfrac{7}{10}$ _____

5. $\dfrac{11}{100}$ _____

6. $\dfrac{19}{100}$ _____

7. $\dfrac{9}{100}$ _____

8. $\dfrac{3}{100}$ _____

9. $\dfrac{21}{100}$ _____

10. $\dfrac{91}{100}$ _____

11. $\dfrac{29}{100}$ _____

12. $\dfrac{7}{100}$ _____

13. $\dfrac{6}{10}$ _____

14. $\dfrac{5}{100}$ _____

15. $\dfrac{2}{10}$ _____

16. $\dfrac{15}{100}$ _____

17. $\dfrac{1}{4}$ _____

18. $\dfrac{1}{2}$ _____

19. $\dfrac{3}{4}$ _____

20. $\dfrac{1}{5}$ _____

21. $\dfrac{2}{5}$ _____

22. $\dfrac{4}{5}$ _____

23. $\dfrac{1}{20}$ _____

24. $\dfrac{5}{20}$ _____

25. $\dfrac{10}{20}$ _____

26. $\dfrac{15}{20}$ _____

27. $\dfrac{5}{25}$ _____

28. $\dfrac{10}{25}$ _____

29. $\dfrac{25}{50}$ _____

30. $\dfrac{10}{50}$ _____

31. $\dfrac{3}{25}$ _____

32. $\dfrac{2}{50}$ _____

Grade 4, Skills Bank
Use any time.

Index of Skills

Addition, 35, 37–42, 54, 55, 56, 154, 156, 157
money numbers, 37, 39, 40, 42, 54, 55, 156, 157
word problems, 39, 40, 54, 56

Area, 61–70

Arrays, 91–93, 101, 107

Capacity, 141, 142, 147, 148

Comparing numbers, 12–14, 20–22, 26

Counting, skip, 11, 23, 44, 47, 121, 125

Data collection, representation, and analysis, 1–5, 7–10

Decimals, 81–84, 87, 88, 181, 182

Division, 45, 46, 48–54, 57, 58, 101–106, 109, 110, 166–171, 176–179
word problems, 53, 54, 58, 103, 104, 110

Estimation skills and strategies, 11, 39, 41, 59, 67–69, 97, 98, 108, 136, 140–144

Fractions, 71–88, 181, 182
comparing, 75, 76, 86
equivalent, 73, 74, 79, 86
part of a set, 77, 78
part of a whole, 71–75, 79–83, 85–88
related to decimals, 79–84, 87, 88, 181, 182

Geometry
lines (intersecting, parallel, perpendicular) 111, 118
location and maps, 116, 117, 120
nets for solids, 114, 119
quadrilaterals, 30–34, 115, 116, 119, 120
solids, 113, 114, 119
squares, 30, 31, 34, 115
symmetry, 112, 118
triangles, 27–29, 33, 34, 64

Graphing, 2, 9, 89, 128

Length, 27, 135–140, 145–147

Line Plots, 3–5, 10

Lines (intersecting, parallel, perpendicular), 111, 118

Location and maps, 116, 117, 120

Mass, 143, 144, 147, 148

Mean, median, mode, and range, 3–7

Measurement
area, 61–70
capacity, 141, 142, 147, 148
comparing measures, 135, 136, 139, 141, 144, 146, 148
length, 27, 135–140, 145–147
mass, 143, 144, 147, 148
perimeter, 59–61, 68, 69

Mental math, 35, 36

Multiplication, 43–47, 49–54, 57, 58, 89–100, 107–110, 160–165, 172–175
word problems, 43, 53, 54, 58, 70, 96, 104, 110

Nets for solids, 114, 119

Numbers (whole)
comparing, 12–14, 20–22, 26
counting, 11, 23, 44, 47, 121, 125
reading and writing, 13–16, 18, 19, 24, 25, 152
representing, 17, 18, 25, 26
rounding, 12, 22, 23, 153

Patterns
multiplication, 95
number, 11, 23, 44, 47, 121, 123–126
shape, 122, 124

Perimeter, 59–61, 68, 69

Place-value concepts, 13–26

Probability concepts, 127–134

Quadrilaterals, 30–34, 115, 116, 119, 120

Skills Bank, 149–182
  addition facts, 154
  addition practice, 156, 157
  decimals, 181, 182
  division facts, 166–171
  division practice, 176–179
  fractions, 181, 182
  multiplication facts, 160–165
  multiplication practice, 172–175
  record chart, 150–151
  rounding numbers, 153
  subtraction facts, 155
  subtraction practice, 158, 159
  time, 180
  writing numbers, 151, 152

Skip Counting, 11, 23, 44, 47

Solids, 113, 114, 119

Squares, 30, 31, 34, 115

Subtraction, 36–42, 54, 55, 56, 155, 158, 159
  money numbers, 37, 42, 54, 55, 159
  word problems, 39, 40, 54, 56

Symmetry, 112, 118

Tables and charts, 2, 4, 7, 9, 17, 21, 22, 27, 33, 34, 42, 67, 97, 101, 104, 115, 122–124, 126, 136

Tallies, 10, 128, 129, 134

Time, 12, 180

Triangles, 27–29, 33, 34, 64

Word problems, 39, 40, 43, 53, 54, 56, 58, 70, 96, 103, 104, 110